M000210214

Carl-Auer

Ilse Kutschera
Christine Brugger

What's Out of Order Here?

Illness and Family Constellations

Translated by Colleen Beaumont

2006

Title of the original edition:
„Was ist nur los mit mir? Krankheitssymptome und Familienstellen"
© 2002 by Kösel-Verlag, München, Germany

DTP: Drißner-Design u. DTP, Meßstetten
Cover: WSP-Design, Heidelberg
Printed by Koninklijke Wöhrmann, Zutphen
Printed in the Netherlands

First edition, 2006
ISBN 13: 978-3-89670-553-2
ISBN 10: 3-89670-553-9

Bibliografic information published by Der Deutschen Bibliothek
Die Deutsche Bibliothek lists this publication
in the Deutschen Nationalbibliografie; detailed bibliografic
data available on Internet http://dnb.ddb.de.

Carl-Auer Verlag
Häusserstraße 14
69115 Heidelberg
Germany
www.carl-auer.com

Table of contents

Acknowledgments

Special thanks goes to my co-author, Christine Brugger, who was out-standing in being able to bring all the complex material I had collected over the years into a readable form. Without her this book would never have been written.

I also would like to thank my friends and colleagues who have constructively helped the emergence of this book: Sabine and Helmut Eichenmüller and Reinhard Weber.

From Dr. Gundl Kutschera, I learned to look towards solutions, and my clients have taught me the complexity of life and a respect for it.

Without the help of eager secretaries, the case studies of the family constellations would not have been completed. I offer my heartfelt thanks to all of them, particularly Bernhild Kathan and Rita Troxler.

Finally, from the bottom of my heart, I would like to thank Bert Hellinger, my teacher and role model. From him I have learned to "acknowledge what is", to look precisely and to keep learning.

Ilse Kutschera
Juli 2006

Introduction

The reason I became a doctor was to help relieve suffering. My primary focus during my medical training was in the area of traditional medicine, but later, in my duties in the hospital it became increasingly, clear to me that my traditional medical approach was not sufficient. I quickly recognised in dealing with patients that the origins of illness and suffering were not always medically diagnosable, but were considerably more complex and required a much broader approach to diagnosis and treatment. "What is the matter with me?" the patients asked, as they travelled with their illnesses and complaints from doctor to doctor, but found no relief.

My father was my role model as a physician, and from him I learned that every patient has to be taken seriously in his or her individual make up. The basic concept of his work was to look at all the essential factors and continue looking until the foreground receded and the full complexity of the illness emerged. Inevitably, my own interests expanded to include psychology along with traditional medical practices.

In my own life the question "What is the matter with me?" also arose, and in addition to the integration of medicine and psychotherapy, I entered a life-long process of psychotherapeutic enquiry and self-development. This is how I came to meet Bert Hellinger in a psychotherapy seminar in 1975. I was fascinated by his precise awareness and his ability to quickly and clearly recognise the essence of an issue. Over a period of 27 years, I participated in many of his seminars. During this time I was able to experience, first hand, his therapeutic developments in family constellations and "movements of the soul".

Good medicine, like good psychotherapy, is based on recognising what really is the matter with a patient. In my experience, family constellations in a therapeutic context are the most effective method towards clarifying what is essential for each individual. Here, it is the unconscious mind that plays the most important role. Since systemic entanglements are unconscious, a therapeutic method is needed that can bring this to light. Bert Hellinger observed and described how invisible bonds in families may have effects over many generations, and in family constellations, he developed a method of making visible those bonds as well as the underlying basic dynamics. This process often allows healing to occur.

In my medical training and practice, I have developed skills in diagnostic observation that can be meaningfully applied in family constellations. Therefore, everything I have learned and experienced flows into my therapeutic work. I find it more satisfying to point towards a path that allows a client to proceed alone than it is to pull someone in a direction that I think would be right for them. Paracelsus said that the patient is his own best doctor, and a doctor only accompanies the patient.

As a doctor and psychotherapist, I am primarily interested in the connections between illness and families. Particularly in acute, serious illness and in chronic disease, it is extremely important to consider entanglements within the family system. Answering the question, "What in the world is the matter with me?" entails following a path that leads from the symptoms towards the family system and then back again.

The physical body provides our most direct expression of the needs of the soul, and when the needs of the soul are ignored, the body begins to cry out. Symptoms appear, seemingly out of nowhere. Accordingly, the focus of this book is on illness and symptoms. Our bodies are our vessels; they are all that we have. As a noted professor once said, "Body and soul are all one and the same."

With the support of Christine Brugger, I am writing this book out of a deep desire to help those who are suffering to find the courage to get to know themselves and their souls and to get a sense of the significance of family entanglements. I hope that many sufferers will find the courage to broaden and deepen their lives through their illness, or with the help of their illness.

What is of Essence?

Illness and Symptoms as Signals

A symptom is defined as "a subjectively perceived problem or complaint reported by the patient". For me, illness and symptoms are signs of a dis-order in life, something that has not been put in order that is being expressed in the physical state. It is largely irrelevant whether a particular organic cause can be determined or not.

Any subjective perception of disturbance is to be taken seriously, whether that involves pain (of organic origin or not) or anxieties (with discernible causes or not). By "taken seriously" I mean paying attention to the causes and effects of all mental and physical symptoms. This serious attention is demanded of the person who is suffering as well as of the one administering treatment. As a cardiologist I have frequently seen subjective, real suffering that was not taken seriously because no organic cause could be determined.

> A 55-year-old woman had been suffering for a year and a half from a disturbing, recurring pain and sense of tightness on the left side of her chest. She came to the university hospital for a heart catheter examination, which showed her heart and coronary arteries to be fully intact. The doctor in charge cheerfully informed the woman that her heart was perfectly healthy. To his surprise, the woman reacted with anger. She was outraged at the results of the examination, because she was suffering from chest pains on a daily basis. This is an example of a discrepancy between organic, determinable causes and subjective suffering. It would have been more beneficial if the physician had given this patient more time and attention following the medical procedure and paid serious attention to her pain, exploring other possible causes of the pain with her, such as difficulties with her children, her partner, and so on.

Unfortunately, from what I have seen, both patients and doctors often regard symptoms with organically determined causes as more worthy of treatment. This value system is also reflected in the usual billing practices in our state health insurance. As a rule, it is much easier to get authorisation for expensive diagnostic measures such as tomography or heart catheterisation, than it is to get payment for psychotherapy. In Germany, insurance funding for psychotherapy is contingent upon a medical referral from the attending physician. A prescription for diagnostic procedures requires only a qualified specialist in that particular area.

The central control for pain, whatever its source, lies in our brain. Regardless whether the headache is organic or mentally caused, the pain is transported by the nerves to the brain where it is experienced and interpreted. Pain, therefore, is always subjective. One of the best examples is back pain. Degeneration in the spine can cause great pain or minor pain, or any degree in between.

> A woman went to visit her godchild, a young woman with whom she had a very loving relationship. The younger woman was in the middle of a marital crisis precipitated by her affair with a lover. Her aunt was successful in getting the married couple into a constructive discussion of the problem, and the niece and her husband resolved to try to work out their relationship difficulties. The next morning, the aunt experienced unbearable back pain. Six weeks later, despite various treatments, the pain remained unchanged. The woman decided to do a constellation in which only she and her symptoms were represented. Following the constellation, the she was free of pain. From a systemic and therapeutic viewpoint, I would diagnose the back pain as pain taken over from someone else. One consequence of the discussion between her niece and her husband was that the niece had to terminate her relationship with her lover. This was a painful separation for the niece, and her aunt lovingly tried to take over some of that pain for her. As always, with feelings taken over from someone else, this all occurred at an unconscious level.

Suffering

People often come to me with hopes of disposing of their suffering, with the expectation that I will make them healthy. My first task is to make it clear that the healing process requires an effort on their part as well. This demand is often met with disbelief' and I have frequently heard from patients, "You must know what is best for me!" Most people coming for psychotherapy, on the other hand, are highly motivated to change something in their lives.

Objectively, most people in our society lead good lives and yet many are suffering. In my profession I have been confronted with much suffering, and I have often wondered why my patients so often seem to hold on so tightly to their suffering. Looking at this issue led me to examine the view of suffering in Christianity. Briefly summarised, we could say, "If I suffer, I am a good person and I will be saved." Who amongst us wouldn't like to be a good person and be saved?

In a group, Bert Hellinger once asked me, "What will happen when you have suffered enough?" I answered, "Well, then I will be saved." His reaction was very sobering. "That is precisely the illusion."

Based on my observations, permission to suffer is much more common than permission to be happy. People become anxious when they experience happiness. Since this way of thinking has been effective for over two thousand years, it would seem to be particularly difficult for us to give up our willingness to suffer.

Nelson Mandela described this phenomenon in the following way: "It is our light and not our darkness that frightens us the most. We ask ourselves: Who am I then, that I should be brilliant, fabulous and healthy? But really, is there any reason not to be? ... That light is not only in some of us, but in every individual. When we let our light shine, we unconsciously give other people permission to do the same."

A fundamental premise of my therapeutic work is that every person is capable of being happy. In a family constellation, a client can leave suffering where it belongs and experience others also responding with joy. Such moments are very touching. Bathed in the joy of their parents, grandparents, siblings, or others, a person feels a greater freedom to be happy.

Fascination with the Role of Victim

In my therapeutic work I have often wondered why it is so difficult for people to give up the role of "victim", and all the suffering that goes with it. There are various theoretical explanations, with some commonalities, all looking at a more or less unconscious level of awareness.

1. Suffering has become a habitual feeling and the person has adjusted his or her life accordingly. The habit is so familiar that there is a feeling of comfort despite the suffering. An end to the suffering requires a change of habits. Such changes may be initiated through conscious decisions or as a result of chance events.
2. For some people, suffering seems to be the only way they can feel anything intensely. "I am suffering so I feel something of myself, therefore I am alive." Suffering becomes their most intense ex-

perience of aliveness. Suffering and aliveness would seem to be contradictory, but this paradox is often seen. When the suffering has subsided, clients often complain of a feeling of emptiness that is difficult to bear.

3. Suffering is rewarded, as in the classic case of the rewards of illness. As long as one suffers, there is more love and attention to be had. Through an illness, such as a heart attack, the patient becomes more important and everything revolves around him or her.

4. Suffering elevates the sufferer to a superior position. Because of the suffering, the person feels superior to others and more demands emerge, usually unconsciously. Because the demands are inappropriate, they cannot be fulfilled, which in turn reinforces the victim-sufferer role. "No one understands me. Everyone is against me." These are the fundamental beliefs of "chronic" victims, who remain in the vicious circle of suffering. In Christianity in particular, there is high value placed on suffering for the sake of others. Martyrdom is a well-known qualification for sainthood.

5. Suffering may be socially recognised and might be a requirement of belonging to a specific group. The "poor abandoned women" are superficially pitied by society, whereas the "abandoned men" have no claim to any social recognition for their suffering. The "abandoned women" form a group who give each other reciprocal pity, affirmation and support. If a woman leaves the role of victim, she cannot continue to belong to this group. Self-help groups also pose a risk because the group identity dictates that only those who suffer can be members.

6. Suffering is characterised by passivity. Casting off this passive state implies becoming active and moving from a victim position to one of perpetrator. Perpetrator, in this positive context, means taking responsibility and moving into action. I have seen that in families entangled with guilt from earlier generations (murder, property theft, and so on), the later sufferers are reluctant to become active. Being unsuccessful and unemployed are symptoms in such cases. Holding on to the victim role is insurance against becoming like a father or grandfather.

7. Inappropriately interpreted, suffering can restore one's innocence. Out of a fear of acknowledging guilt, someone may retreat into the role of victim and thus appear to be innocent. For example, we can look at the role of many in the Third Reich who, after the war,

took on the role of victims and "weren't involved". In this case the role of victim was almost a mass phenomenon and was socially respectable for a long time. The refusal to acknowledge guilt has consequences for those in later generations who take over the suffering.

8. As a balance for the earlier perpetrators' unacknowledged guilt, later family members often feel guilty without any cause. Out of loyalty to the victims of their ancestors, these current family members feel like traitors if they abandon their victim role. Only when there is freedom to love the perpetrators and feel sympathy with the victims can the crimes be left with the actual perpetrators and later descendents be free of the pressure to make themselves into victims. The descendents of the earlier victims also remain in a victim role out of loyalty to their ancestors. The symptoms of these sufferers are similar, namely serious illness and depression.

In addition, we could name other forms of "self-sacrifice" adopted by many. I would include groups such as Doctors without Borders, disaster workers in similar organisations, charity workers, etc. The goal of these volunteer or minimally paid helpers is "to do good".

What prompts a young woman to work as a nurse in a minefield in Angola? What moves a 39-year-old teacher to teach illiterate people in Africa? Each has perhaps given up personal security, money and possibly even family and relationships in order to serve the needy. The sacrifice may be serving as a kind of reparations within their own system or in a larger, social context. A family constellation can often show the dynamics and how that may be bringing healing into the system.

The Meaning of Illness

I am convinced that there is meaning to be found behind every symptom and every illness. This is not a meaning that is applicable to life in general, but one that is always subjective and dependent upon the situation of the patient and the relationships in that person's system. You cannot say, for example, that headaches mean that someone is hitting their head against a brick wall about something. Actually, headache could mean many different things, depending on the conditions under which the person has headache and what the effects are on the patient and his or her surroundings. The meaning of an illness is individually determined and cannot be generalised. I would go one step further and propose that any patient can find meaning in his or her illness. The sense of it can be made conscious with the help of a family constellation.

In dealing with the meaning of illness, there are some basic principles, but no recipes, for transforming the meaning of symptoms into healing energy. According to our modern orientation towards effort and achievement, searching for the meaning of an illness is often interpreted as, "If you are ill, there is something you have to learn." This is, however, a misunderstanding.

Such a forced, externally dictated interpretation may increase a person's feeling of guilt in some cases, but offers nothing more. The meaning I am talking about, which I have seen and experienced in family constellations, goes far beyond this. It is an expression of systemic entanglements that have developed out of love. This is quite different from "having something to learn" in the sense of a task to be accomplished.

Illness and Death

There is a great difference between an illness that is potentially fatal, such as cancer, and an illness that "only" causes suffering, for example, neurodermatitus. The difference lies in an awareness of one's own mortality. Potentially fatal illnesses are always more serious because they are nearer to death. As a rule, one could say that the more serious the illness, the deeper the entanglements, and therefore, the greater the loyalty to the system. The potential for therapy is limited in such cases and I have learned to respect what cannot be changed in those situations. As a physician and therapist, I always find this difficult.

In the case of a serious, perhaps fatal, illness, it can be helpful to simply acknowledge "what is". Even when healing is not possible, there still may be an opportunity for a patient to make useful changes in attitude. When someone has acknowledged that his or her illness is leading towards death, that person lives more intensely, more richly and with increased clarity for the time that life is still available.

It was through accompanying dying patients that I first deeply faced the truth that we all must die, whether we have an organic illness or not. I have learned from these patients that looking at death intensifies life, and accepting its finality changes the quality of life. It also changes the quality of the dying and of saying goodbye.

> A woman with a serious heart disease did a constellation of herself, Death and Life. Life was only able to look at the woman kindly after Death had been properly acknowledged and honoured. (See complete description of Susanne's constellation on page 81.

Aside from one's birth, death is the most important thing in life. As Bert Hellinger remarked, "Bonds are to freedom as limits are to fullness." If I look at death as the limit of life, which is what I would judge it to be, then an awareness of the end is essential if we are to enjoy the fullness of life and to live. I have met many people who say, "When I am sixty, then I'm going to do this, that, or the other" or "When I retire, then I'll be able to do something." Many people postpone life in this way rather than living each day. As a rule, it is impossible to change gears at retirement age. You are just as incapable of enjoying life after you stop working as you were before. Sometimes death interferes with those kinds of plans because the meaning of life seems to be gone when the working phase of life is past. Recognising the finality of life not only brings grief for what is past and what hasn't been experienced, but it also makes it possible to enjoy the fullness of life in each present moment.

Death is a taboo topic, one that raises anxiety. In family constellations, we handle death in a normalised fashion. We bring it into the picture because it is unavoidable and a part of our lives. If you face death, you discover that it is friendly, not evil. In Schubert's song *Death and the Maiden* Death says to a young, dying girl, "Be of good cheer. I am not wild. You shall sleep gently in my arms".

In my first family constellations, I was afraid to set up a representative for death. Once I had faced the finality of life myself, I could handle the topic and this figure of death. It often happens that adding death to a constellation has a relieving effect. Death always appears untroubled and friendly. There was a constellation involving two men, both of whom were cancer patients in the final stage of the illness.

> One of the men was 45 years old and the father of five children. The other was only 32 years old and had one small child. In the constellation it was clear that death was nearby and that the men would die, which

both of them had already known beforehand. What was new for them was experiencing the friendliness and peacefulness of death. Both of their wives said later that their husbands had died peacefully at home, without undue suffering and without any life-prolonging measures.

It is particularly tragic when a child is lost in a family system. In this situation too, a family constellation can bring about reconciliation with fate. When grieving parents have an experience of death as unavoidable and a new dimension opens up, they may be able to say goodbye to their child in peace and harmony. It is almost impossible to describe this sense of harmony, but the following example is an illustration.

> A woman had lost her only son in an accident at age 15. He had been run over by a bus and killed, and his mother was filled with hate towards the bus driver. In the constellation, I placed the boy's death behind the bus driver. In this configuration, the mother felt the death of her son move into another dimension. The bus driver led to a dimension that we cannot understand, but can only agree to. The boy's mother agreed to this image, her hate disappeared and she felt calm.

Before I did this constellation, I had qualms about my therapeutic task. Was it right to confront a grieving mother with that terrible event, or would it be too much for her? The result of the constellation confirmed that letting in what is unchangeable, "what is", is precisely what brings peace.

The Meaning of Health

Once, in an advanced training group for physicians, we made the astounding discovery that we all had difficulty with the term "health", although we were all engaged in daily efforts to promote it.

How could we promote something if we didn't even know what it was? The result was a very in-depth discussion about what "health" means. We all agreed that health is primarily a subjective experience of well-being. This means that a patient might feel healthy despite the presence of illness and symptoms. Health and illness need not be contradictory in a subjective experience and do not necessarily create a polarity, as it is often thought.

My definition of health is: *I am healthy when I live with my abilities and possibilities in such a way that I feel satisfied with myself and with my ionships with others.* To state it boldly, organic health may be secondary. An illustration of this occurred when I was an assistant physician at a university hospital in Munich.

A woman came in once a month for a phlebotomy procedure. She had a congenital heart defect and had been operated on twice. She was not a candidate for another operation and she knew that she did not have long to live. She was also aware that she would not be able to have children, as it would be potentially fatal for her. Her physical capabilities were so limited that when climbing stairs, she had to stop every two steps to catch her breath.

She was introduced to medical students during a lecture presentation. At the end of the session, the head doctor asked the students what they had noticed about this woman. The students duly described her organic symptoms. He then asked the patient about her life style. She replied that she was happily married and, although she could not have children, there were many children in her circle of friends. During the questioning, the patient seemed very calm and at peace. She then left the lecture hall. The professor then asked the students what they had seen in this woman that was of fundamental importance. The students were unable to identify what that was. The professor then provided the answer himself. "I will tell you. This woman has agreed to the limits of her life and has filled her life in a better way than many who are physically healthy."

The implications do not seem to fit with our contemporary concept of health, which is often equated with fitness and vitality. That definition of health implies the dream of eternal youth and capabilities and negates the finality of life. From birth to death, our life is a process that demands our consent. Bert Hellinger described what it is that we generally do: "Running away from death, we run right into his arms."

The Heart

The primary cause of death in Germany continues to be heart attack. Despite all our knowledge, 300,000 people die each year of coronary heart disease. The numbers have remained constant for the last twenty years, in spite of the extensive information presented in lectures and at conferences. We have to ask, "Why?" One possible explanation is the increasing "heartlessness" of our times. I have noticed that feelings such as love and loyalty have now been relegated to the category of "kitsch" and have lost their depth. On the other hand, the fundamental need for nourishing love is granted less and less space in our actual life plans. The yearning for love has been successfully marketed, and we compensate for our lack with greed for "more and more" and with consumerism.

American studies on the structure of the personality in heart attack patients revealed the primary defining factor as hostility and an on-going, latent aggression. These results correspond to my own experience. It would appear that heart patients find it easier to get angry and upset than to allow feelings such as grief and joy. Where does this hostility come from? In my opinion, it serves to protect against deeper underlying pain. In the final analysis, some of my patients would rather die than face their pain.

The following example shows the healing effects brought about by experiencing the pain of an untimely death of a mother.

In 1991, a 52-year-old man came to me with a serious heart condition. Of the three coronary blood vessels that supply the heart with blood, two were closed, and he was surviving with only one coronary blood vessel. The patient declined to have a proposed operation and my colleagues' prognosis was a life expectancy of a year or two. The patient was married and worked as a patent attorney. His wife had had six miscarriages and the couple had adopted two children. Through the circumstances of her husband's heart attack, the patient's wife unexpectedly discovered that he had had a second, "quasi-marriage" for the past eighteen years. This revelation led to a major life crisis, and the man decided to go into psychotherapy. Of course he had a rationale for his double relationships; one woman was his housewife, the other his lover. For a long time this rationale had kept him from becoming aware of his deeper yearning for love.

Course of Therapy: When I think back on this man, the beginning of the therapy was what made the strongest impression on me. Even before the man sat down, as we were greeting each other and shaking hands, he began to speak. "Now I can say that my mother was a Jew and died in 1936 at the age of 28. I was two and a half years old at the time." Although his father had married three more times, the client was his only child.

The man came for individual therapy regularly over the next two years. In my view, the most important factor during this phase of the therapy was for me to maintain my relationship (transference mother) with him. During this time the client was gradually able to sense his own deep longing for closeness. His double relationships had made it possible for him to avoid confronting any need for intimacy and had minimised the risk of loss. As he became more aware of his longing, he also realised that his relationships with two women had prevented a deep closeness with either.

In my opinion, the cause of his symptoms lay in the early loss of his mother. As therapist, I would say that he was remaining true to his mother. He tried to prevent, at all costs, any further pain of loss. The deepest love of a child, the love for his mother, had been abruptly interrupted by her death.

In addition to individual therapy, the client participated in group sessions for heart patients that focussed primarily on self-awareness. After six years, he was finally ready to take part in a family constellation. It took him that long to overcome his fear of experiencing the pain of his loss.

The constellation consisted of him and his mother. They stood facing one another. The representative of his mother spontaneously opened her arms to him and looked at him lovingly. It was clear to me that the client was torn between his fear and his longing for closeness. His inner struggle went on for some minutes, and then he fell into his mother's arms and wept. Beaming, she held him tightly in her arms. His love for his mother that had been interrupted was opened up again. At this point, the therapy, which had lasted over six years, was at an end.

This constellation took place ten years ago. The patient is still alive and enjoying life. He is overweight and pays no attention to his cholesterol levels.

My hypothesis in this case is that the patient was able to re-establish his love for his mother once he had recognised and experienced the enormous pain of his loss. The love between children and their parents is an emotional bond that holds fast beyond separation and death. This deep bond affects our entire life and influences our ability to love other people, and therefore affects all later relationships and partnerships.

After experiencing his pain in the family constellation and re-opening his love for his mother, the client remained healthy. This primary, interrupted love for his mother almost caused his death, because if he had died of his heart disease he would have been near her again.

As a consequence, the man was able to satisfy his longing for intimacy with his wife and was ready to slowly and gently end the extra-marital relationship. It would have been useless to push him to choose one of the women or the other without any awareness of the original cause of his behaviour.

As we can see, the heart is not just a symbol for love, but is organically bound to love. When love has been interrupted (in Hellinger's words "an interrupted reaching-out movement") the patient needs to pick up the thread from that point in time in order to find healing. As a cardiologist, I wish that these connections were more widely recognised and treated. Since modern medicine can mechanically treat heart disease very well, it leads many patients to feel that they only have a heart problem, but otherwise are healthy and if their heart is repaired, everything will be fine. In my opinion, a lasting cure only occurs when the systemic entanglements that have contributed to the illness have been resolved.

Relationships

Relationships in Family Systems

The topic of relationships has been important throughout time and continues to be so. In the natural sciences, there is an increasing interest in the inter-relationship of everything in nature, in all humanity and in the reciprocal nature of these connections. We can only exist when all of our organs are functioning in harmony with one another. To ensure our well being, every organ must fulfil its own task in its own place. Something very similar is true of the family. The relationships and positions of the individual family members are critically important to the well-being of the entire family system.

A diseased heart is connected to the whole body and influences the functioning of the other organs such as kidneys, lungs and brain. In the same way, the illness of one family member influences all the relationships in the person's social systems, including family, friends and co-workers. From what I have observed in traditional medical practices, these relationships are usually completely ignored. An initial intake interview in modern medicine is primarily concerned with symptoms and at best looks at the patient as an individual. It is rarely noted how the illness or symptoms have altered the relationship of the patient to his or her partner, children, friends or colleagues.

A significant factor that frequently appears is some "profit" from the illness, which usually takes the form of increased attention from others. If, because of this illness, a patient is receiving loving attention that would otherwise be missing, a doctor is going to have great difficulty influencing the course of the illness. This is often an important factor in chronic illness. Sometimes the patient cannot find any way other than illness to communicate within his or her relationship systems. The patient, however, often has no conscious awareness of any gain.

> A 70-year-old woman came to our hospital with a heart condition. She subjectively felt much more fragile than would have been expected from the indications of the objective examination. When confronted with the discrepancy, the woman stated, "If I weren't so weak, none of my children would come to see me." All of her children were invited to come to the hospital, and we encouraged the patient to tell her children what she really wanted from them. The most amazing thing, also for the doctors present, was the children's reaction. They were delighted to finally hear clearly from their mother what it was she expected of them. As a result, a schedule of their visits to their mother and the responsibilities of each child were clearly defined. Everyone knew who was to come when and who was to do what. The patient's condition improved immediately. With no increase in medication, she was able to do things that had previously been impossible, such as climbing three flights of stairs.

My explanation for the change is that the patient learned that if she told her children clearly what she needed, she would get it from them. It was no longer necessary for her to be demonstrably weak and fragile. On the other hand, the children were pleased and free of guilt. They were happy to be able to give to their mother something that had become increasingly difficult as her suffering had increased. When their mother could thankfully accept what they had to offer, the children were able to provide the kind of support that contributed to the well being of the entire family.

Illness that springs from entanglements in the family system are much more difficult for a physician to identify. They often originate in previous generations, are usually at an unconscious level and stem from love for the family or for a particular family member.

A complete initial case history may give some indications of possible entanglements. An effective psychotherapeutic approach is needed to help the patient become aware of these issues and to integrate them into the healing process. In my experience, family constellations are the most effective method of resolving such entanglements.

Couple Relationships

I would like to look more closely at one of the relationships in a system, the "couple" relationship between two people. These days, a couple's relationship usually begins with love, or more accurately, being "in love". There is nothing that is so talked about, dreamed about, and fantasised about as the love between partners. Although the word love is bandied about continually in everyday life, there are enormous, usually unconscious, differences in our understanding of it. Therefore, I will define the term "love" as I understand it, with attention to the grave difference between "loving" and "being in love".

Falling in love is something that happens suddenly. We experience it as a spontaneous reaction to a person, and it is accompanied by physiological and hormonal changes that feel stimulating. This "being in love" between two partners has a lot in common with the unconditional love of a child for its mother. In a certain sense, a child is just as blind towards his or her mother as are people "in love". The lovers' feelings of dependency illustrate another parallel with the mother-child relationship. A child is existentially dependent upon its mother to fulfil all needs. If the child is not cared for, he or she will die. The longing for this security, safety and care is unconsciously played out again in the lovers' relationship. This is why there are people for whom a separation from their partner is experienced as an existential threat: "If you leave me I will die."

"Being in love is blind – loving is seeing": a few words from Bert Hellinger that capture the difference between the two. A love that is awake sees the other as he or she is and loves that person as a complete individual. Love leaves room for the other person and for that person's fate. The loved one is strengthened. I always ask my clients, "Does this love strengthen you or weaken you?" When such questions are understood and taken seriously, the answers are spontaneous and reveal the essential quality of that particular love.

A woman had been married for 28 years and had two grown children. She fell head over heels in love with another man, moved in with him and got a divorce within six weeks. She was very convincing when she told me that she was happier than she had ever been before in her life. However, since her two children were not doing very well, she joined a couples' therapy group. In the first round I asked her, "Does this love strengthen you or weaken you?" Her answer was immediate: "It weakens me." She talked in the group about how her husband had dealt with the situation. He felt that if this new love was right for her, she had to go that direction and he wouldn't stand in her way. He also told her that the door was always open for her to come back.

After a year, the client decided to leave her lover and give her old relationship another chance. The decision was made first in her own soul, that is, she did not return to her ex-husband, but lived alone for a while. She had become aware of the difference between being in love and loving.

A basic principle of my work is that love brings strength to the loved one, primarily at the deep level of the soul. A relationship that mostly serves to satisfy personal needs such as financial support or an avoidance of being alone, or one that exploits dependency usually weakens the partner. "I love you," often means, "I want something more from you." The something more may be more attention, more support, more understanding, and so on. Such needs exist, of course, and can be met in a satisfying relationship with a good balance between giving and taking.

Marriage broadens the functions of a relationship to include children. According to Bert Hellinger, marriage is primarily intended to pass life on. In this sense, marital love can be seen as a shared vision of the future. In the words of Antoine de Saint-Exupéry, "Love does not mean looking at one another, but rather looking in the same direction."

At the same time, a marriage of two people also broadens the relationship to include the original family systems of each partner. The values and traditions of both family systems flow into the marriage, as well as the burdens of those systems. If these influences remain unconscious, they may have a destructive effect on the marriage and lead to a separation. This is why it is so important to look at the original family systems of both partners when there are difficulties in a marriage. Using a family constellation to look at these issues can resolve many marital crises. It requires mutual respect from both partners and a respect for the origins of each.

A woman reported in a seminar that her nine-year-old daughter was suffering from a brain tumour. The mother wanted to do a family constellation to see whether her daughter was carrying some burden from her or from her husband that might be contributing to her health problems. It was clear in the constellation that the child's disease had some connection to her father. The mother was very distressed because it seemed to her that there was no way that she could help her daughter. I suggested that she tell her husband about the experience.

As a result, the father came to do a constellation. He said that his wife had told him that his daughter's illness seemed to have something to do with him and his family of origin. During the constellation, I asked him what had happened to his mother, and he revealed that his mother had committed suicide when he was fourteen years old. It was clear in the constellation that his daughter felt drawn to her grandmother, thereby taking over the urge that really belonged to her father. The man was able to take in the pain and loss of his mother and to honour her death, which released his daughter.

In this case I was very touched by the seriousness of both the parents and particularly the father's unconditional willingness to do whatever was possible for his child. His wife had told him about her experience and he respected what she felt and accepted it, which led to a resolution. I can't emphasise enough the importance of respect and acknowledgement of one's partner and their experience, thoughts and feelings.

Relationships in Social Systems

Systems and relationships are interwoven. Every system is a result of relationships and is defined by their limits. Within these limits, there are certain rules that guarantee each member's right to belong to the system. Each individual is also connected to other systems of relationships, which are similarly defined by different limits and rules. Every person lives in a variety of social systems, each of which follows its own set of rules. If the rules of the system are ignored, the individual may be excluded from that social group.

For example, a person belongs simultaneously to the social systems of family and of work. These two systems are separated from each other by space and content and in their organisation. At the same time, they come into reciprocal contact with one another through the members of the systems. There are different rules in the work place, for example, about authority or the use of power; a family system may demand a loving, caring father. It might be very strange for workers to experience their boss in his role of family father, just as his children would not want to be faced with their father in his possibly authoritarian role as the boss. When the rules get confused, problems result.

Another example of laws within a system comes from my experience as a physician and psychotherapist in a cardiac rehabilitation clinic. The rules within the group of medical doctors are different from the rules in the psychotherapists' group. As a senior physician, in order to belong to the group of other senior physicians, I had to respect their rules and behave accordingly, one of which was wearing a white coat during ward rounds.

I preferred to wear my normal clothes rather than a white coat during rounds, as would be normal in a psychotherapeutic context. My intention in this action was to disrupt the classic doctor-patient relationship, to reduce the patients' anxiety and to encourage a more open communication with them. My behaviour violated the rules of the physician group and was seen as disloyalty to the group. They treated me, therefore, like a traitor and some of them shut me out completely. Not one followed my example. It was only later that I became aware of the systemic logic and the resulting consequences of my actions.

The system I am talking about in this book is the family system in the broadest sense of the word, the system of the whole "clan". The boundaries of this system are defined by the phenomenon of bonds. Those who belong to the system include parents, their siblings and children, grandparents and their siblings and children, and any previous partners and their children. Relationships exist, not only between blood relatives, but also through marriage and other additions to the family, such as adopted children or foster children. It also includes extra-marital relationships and any children resulting from such liaisons. This is the broadest possible sense of a family group, which includes all those who have been taken in.

Family systems are also interrelated with other family systems through relationships. When two people marry, the two family systems are connected and there are effects in both systems. At the same time, any family members who have been excluded, ignored, or whose very existence has been denied, are still part of the family system. The phenomenon of this bond to the system can have powerful effects: there may be feelings that have been taken over from other members, guilt or some particularly difficult fate, that show up in the system lategr in a disruptive way. Family constellations offer a way to reveal these effects and resolve entanglements.

Basic Principles of Family Constellations

Bonds

The most fundamental aspect of these bonds is that they exist whether we want them to or not. At the moment of conception, a bond is formed between the child and his or her parents. When we separate from our parents, even if all contact is broken off, the bond to our parents remains. The bonds will have effects on our lives, and there is no way for us to consciously influence those effects.

Bonds exist between all members of a clan, but the connection between children and their parents is the strongest. This is a force that can overcome even a fear of death, which sometimes leads to a child's death, a movement of the child's love for his or her parents. (See the example of Anna, p. **) This bond of love also explains the loyalty of abused children to their parents; they cannot be disloyal. When children are forced into a situation that requires them to be disloyal, such as testifying in court or in an investigation process, it can destroy them. As Bert Hellinger says, "Bonds to the system are stronger than a fear of death."

Order

The concept of order seems simple to explain. It means that the first is in first place, the second in second place, and so on.

These days, the principle of order has special significance, since many men and women have more than one marriage or relationship. A second partnership can only succeed if the first is acknowledged and honoured as the first.

In the sequence of children, the eldest is first in the hierarchy. Traditionally, the eldest child used to be entitled to take over the family estate, which implied rights and responsibilities. For many centuries, everyone generally accepted the validity of this order. When the basic hierarchical order is disrupted, for example through an unjust inheritance, it often brings difficulties for the person who has unjustly profited.

The reality of this order means that parents can never treat each of their children exactly the same, since each is born into a different situation. The timing and sequence of birth determines the placement of each child in the family. In modern families, a stepchild may change the apparent sequence of the children. The eldest son has suddenly got an elder sister and seems to be demoted from his place. The essential fact is that this son remains the first born for his mother even though a stepsister has taken the place as eldest in the new family. Behavioural problems in children can often be resolved when the hierarchical order is made clear. It is also possible to keep the sequential order clear and visible in everyday situations, such as seating positions at the dinner table.

When looking at two separate systems, however, the order is different. In this case, the newer, current system has priority over the previous system. The present family has priority over one's family of origin. When conflicts arise, a spouse takes priority over parents. For example, if a man's wife is having difficulties with her in-laws, the man owes his support to his wife. If he takes his mother's side instead of his wife's, it disrupts the order of priority of the new system over the old, and the marriage is in grave danger. The priority of systems can be explained biologically, since the son is now an adult and can only ensure the continuation of the family with his wife, not with his parents.

When there are multiple relationships involving children, the newest system has priority over previous ones. If a married man has a child with another woman, this new extra-marital family takes priority over his marriage. Although it may seem contradictory, the first partner and children must still be acknowledged and honoured as first, and they retain their position as such. In contrast to the common practice of denigrating a previous partner in order to relieve guilt, the solution lies in respecting and honouring that partner. "Thank you for everything you have given me." Then, the new relationship has a systemic basis for success.

The relationship between children from a previous relationship and a new partner is a particularly delicate one. Children from an earlier relationship take priority over a later partner. In my experience, conflicts between new partners and their stepchildren can be avoided if the original parents give their children the security of knowing that their place in the hierarchy will be maintained and respected, even in the new situation.

Children have to respect their parents' decision to form new relationships and have no right to sabotage this choice. They will be less likely to attempt to do so if their mother or father is clearly standing by the new partner. In this way a relationship can grow and a positive spiral is nurtured.

These structures that Bert Hellinger has observed and described provide a useful perspective for looking at order within a family system. Dealing with them requires sensitivity and respect on the part of everyone involved. When the order of the system is disrupted, the results are quarrels, jealousy and suffering. It is clear that these guidelines will provoke objections since they seem very rigid, but my experience has been that respect for systemic order promotes peace and healing. This stance is often only possible with therapeutic support.

Balance in Taking and Giving

A balance of taking and giving is of essence and, here again, sequence is important. Taking comes first. Only when I have taken can I also give. Of particular importance is taking life from one's parents, just as it is given. There is a balance of taking and giving in every relationship: in the family, amongst friends, and in work relationships. Money is one currency for giving and taking, but care, attention, and recognition are also gifts.

An imbalance in giving and taking can destroy a relationship. The critical word here is balance. When one person gives too much, for example a very expensive present, the receiver feels unable to reciprocate, and that feeling can destroy the relationship. The one who has been given too much will feel uncomfortable with this sense of debt and may pull back from the giver.

The situation is quite different between parents and children. Parents always give more and children always take more. Balance is achieved over generations in a family. Children take from their parents and give to their own children, and balance is maintained in the family system over a longer period of time.

The Golden Ball

For the love my father gave to me
I did not give him due.
As child, I didn't know the value of the gift.
As man, became too hard, too like a man.
My son is growing to manhood now, loved with passion
as no other, present in his father's heart.
I give of that which I once took, to one from
whom it did not come, nor is it given back.

When he becomes a man, thinking as a man,
he will, as I, follow his own path.
I'll watch with longing free from envy as
he gives on to his own son the love I gave to him.
My gaze follows the game of life
deep through the halls of time—
each smilingly throws the golden ball,
and no one throws it back
to him from whom it came.

Börries von Münchhausen

A balance between giving and taking also plays an important role at another level of family systems. When one member of a family incurs a debt or guilt (for example, as a result of actions during a war), it often happens that later family members suffer for it in some form. But, paradoxically, if one member of a family has suffered some terrible stroke of fate, it is also later suffering that re-establishes systemic balance. Both suffering and guilt within the family system are balanced out over many generations, and all the members of the clan are affected.

Attempts to correct imbalance in the system may appear as severe mental disturbances, physical symptoms, or serious illnesses. I have seen seriously depressed patients who have tried a variety of therapeutic approaches, without relief from their symptoms. Their family histories are often quite similar: one member of the family suffered a terrible blow of fate in the past, or another incurred some guilt. Experience has shown that the descendents of victims and perpetrators, that is, their children and grandchildren, suffer from similar symptoms and illnesses. Guilt or suffering that has been taken over by a later member of the family expresses itself either in physical disease, such as cancer, multiple sclerosis or heart disease, or in a mental disturbances such as a therapy-resistant depression.

> A woman in a therapy group was very politically active, as both her mother and her grandmother had been. This political and social commitment wove through three generations like a repeating theme. The client came seeking relief from a medically untreatable back pain. In the family constellation, it became clear that something terrible must have happened in an earlier generation. When the client asked her mother about this, she reported that four or five generations earlier, a woman in the family had arranged for her lover to kill her husband so that she could then marry her lover. As recompense for this crime, the women in the following generations had become very involved in political and social issues. After my client had unearthed this information, we did another constellation. I asked her to bow down before all of these women to honour their attempts to pay for the guilt of their ancestor. I believe that my client's back pain had also originated as recompense for that historical crime. That hypothesis has been borne out by the fact that the woman has enjoyed relief from her physical complaints ever since that constellation.

A central issue in taking and giving is the acceptance of life, just as it is given by one's parents. There is actually no other option, since the conditions are dictated by circumstance. Consenting to this is an essential prerequisite for happiness. "I take this life, just as it has been given to me." Although the logic seems very simple, the application is often extremely difficult. Honouring your father and mother in this way does not mean agreeing with all of their actions. It means taking and treasuring that which they could give and have given. Refusing to accept what has been given may create feelings of superiority. "If you take, you are in debt." By this, Bert Hellinger did not mean debt in its narrowest sense, but rather, an obligation to balance the taking in some way. If you refuse to take, you have no debt and have no obligations. To all appearances you are then free. The lack, however, fosters demands for something more: more money, more understanding, more support, a different childhood, a different kind of love, and so on. These demands can never be met in relationships, so they continue to create dissatisfaction and feelings of deprivation. Those feelings, in turn, feed new demands.

All relationships function through taking and giving. When one person refuses to take the love that is given and instead fills the need with material goods, the relationship is endangered. We have all met people who are never satisfied with what they have and make material belongings more and more central. Life, love and loyalty, however, are not for sale. Material consumption that has been prompted by these needs is a substitute for taking in a relationship and precludes a sense of satisfaction. In Bert Hellinger's words, "Greed is wanting to have without taking."

Relationships are nourished by each partner taking, with gratitude, what is given and giving back, with love, more than has been taken.

Thanking is one form of restoring balance. You can only thank, however, if you have first taken. We have all had the experience of giving a present that is received with joy and thanks. How does that feel, as the giver? Does it restore an appropriate balance? But we are also familiar with the opposite, when a gift is rejected or discounted. What does that feel like? Is balance restored?

One of the basic forms of restoring balance is giving thanks with gratitude. As a therapist, I often suggest that people write a letter of thanks to their father, mother, former partner or friend. I asked one heart patient, who was unable to accept his father, to write his father a thank you letter. I never saw the patient again, but happened to hear about him from his doctor, whom he had told about my recommendation. Although the man thought it was a quite a useless thing to do, he wrote the letter. The results were rather unexpected, and since that time he has got on with his father much better. In this case there were no dramatic medical effects, but I like to think back on this man, because his story illustrates how the basic principle of balance functions, even if the person involved doesn't really believe in it.

Negative Balance

The balance of giving and taking can function negatively as well as positively. In the negative sense, if you have had to endure some injury or insult, or if you feel at the mercy of someone else and have suffered for it, there have to be consequences for the person who has caused the suffering. Forgiving too quickly, or lacking the courage to demand that the other person suffer, creates a feeling of superiority. This imbalance will disrupt the relationship in the future. Balance has to be restored before the relationship can move on to a new level.

In order to avoid a negative spiral of escalation ("I'll do to you what you have done to me!") it is important to inflict a bit less pain than what has been received.

Bert Hellinger has said that "It is only possible for two people to return to equilibrium with one another when both have suffered equally."

The Function of Conscience

Bonds and Conscience

A need to belong is basic to every person. Belonging to a family is essential for survival.

Conscience functions like an instrument of awareness for the soul, one that allows you to sense which actions ensure your right to belong and which actions endanger your place in the group. Bert Hellinger has stated that the function of the systemic conscience has nothing to do with morals in the usual sense of the word. We have all been taught that if we do good things we will have a clear conscience and if we do bad things we will have a guilty conscience. In contrast, Bert Hellinger's almost revolutionary statement is, "The worst actions can be performed with a clear conscience."

Systemic conscience functions to ensure our belonging to our family and to various other groups that we belong to in the course of our lives. The need to belong ranks above all others and is controlled by this conscience. This is why conscience has to function differently in different groups. We have a different conscience when it comes to our parents than in our work situation. We might value certain behaviours positively in our family that we would assess negatively in a work team. For example, in our family we might expect closeness and attention, and when we take time for personal conversations, we have a clear conscience. The same behaviour in the office could provoke a guilty conscience.

Depending on which group we owe our loyalty to, it is possible to do terrible things with a clear conscience. This must have been the case with members of the SS during the Third Reich, who committed murder with a "clear" conscience.

Conscience is the basis for our loyalty to a group or to our clan. When I ask clients in a therapy group, "What did your grandfather do in World War Two?" it seems that no one did anything bad. Children and grandchildren are loyal and follow the conscience of their father or grandfather, who did not have a guilty conscience about killing people in wartime.

When we want to free ourselves from our family's entanglements, we usually have a bad conscience. Even asking about one's grandfather's role in the war may provoke outrage, "How can you even ask that?" and then the person who is probing feels bad. Grandfather's memory has been besmirched in some way and the one who brought up the question feels compelled to justify it, which causes a guilty conscience. This can go as far as making the person feel like a traitor to the family system, and he or she will be treated accordingly. There will be no more questions about grandfather's war experience, the person will return to a loyal position and will remain trapped in the entanglements.

Freeing oneself from entanglements often means suffering a guilty conscience, and it is crucial to understand this fact. In family constellations, it is sometimes very difficult for clients to withstand the pangs of conscience, and it may happen that following a resolving constellation the client feels bad about it. It often helps when I explain the connection between a bad conscience and the resolving of entanglements and point out possible effects. As a therapist I make myself available to offer clients support following a constellation.

The bonds that exist in every system are central to the loyalty of the group members. An individual cannot really survive alone; we need groups and we need relationships. There are particular rules in each system that determine belonging to that particular group. If someone follows the rules, they have a clear conscience. When the rules are broken, for example, asking what happened during the war, the person has a bad conscience.

The bond to one's family is a given, an unchangeable reality, but bonds to other groups may be temporary, as in a work group or school class. When I feel like a member of a group, conscience functions just as it does in the family. Belonging to my family lasts my entire life and I cannot separate from it, but when I leave a work group or other temporary group, I often experience a guilty feeling towards that group. The function is the same, but with the basic difference that the bonds are much stronger within the family system than in any other group.

Conscience and Order

When conscience is functioning in service to bonds, it keeps people trapped in their entanglements. When conscience is serving order, it has quite a different effect. Here, a bad conscience is the watchdog for the continuance of order and has positive consequences. If someone violates the orders of relationships by showing a lack of respect for a previous partner, for example, that person feels guilty. Often, the person then quashes the guilty feelings by denigrating the previous partner even more strongly. The only thing that can resolve this negative spiral is to restore order with respect and recognition of the previous partner.

Inheritance situations often illustrate a violation of order. If there has been an unjust legacy, the one who benefits can restore balance by showing generosity towards those who were disadvantaged. His or her conscience will then be clear, and the relationship between the family members will remain intact. If the beneficiary, however, insists upon seizing the gains and ignores the pangs of conscience, the family relationships will be damaged. In some situations, such disagreements may lead to long-term feuds in which future generations are no longer on speaking terms with other members of the family. A violation of the orders has continuing effects and a family constellation can bring these to light and provide resolution.

Conscience and Balance

Conscience serves to restore order. When a balance of taking and giving is involved, conscience has a similarly constructive function. A bad conscience makes itself felt through a guilty feeling. In everyday life, we use phrases such as, "I owe you one", or "I'm very indebted to you." It means that the person who has received something feels a debt as long as the taking has not been balanced out by some kind of giving. It may be that repayment is not possible at that moment. A feeling of guilt or indebtedness is experienced as discomfort and usually avoided. Someone may try to remain free from debt by refusing to take anything or by devaluing the gift or the giver, thereby maintaining a clear conscience.

An example: A family goes on holiday and asks the neighbour's children to care for their cat. When they return, they have forgotten to bring the children a thank you present and they feel guilty about their carelessness. There are two possible options. The first is to go and get a present and settle the debt. Balance is restored and they will have a clear conscience and can ask the children to do it again the following year. A less desirable response is to devalue the debt. "Well, that's the least they can do as neighbours." The balance of giving and taking is skewed and their relationship with their neighbours will deteriorate. The tiny incidents that contribute to the deterioration of a relationship often seem so insignificant that we cannot even remember them later. We have all had this experience, even though it is a simple matter to pay attention to maintaining a good balance of taking and giving.

The most essential function of the systemic conscience, therefore, is to support relationships.

Experience with Family Constellations

The Round

Having experienced rounds many times in Bert Hellinger's seminars, I have adopted the practice in my own work. In a round, each member of the group, in turn, has a chance to say something. They can say what is on their mind, and what issues they have brought with them. The therapist, and only the therapist, responds to what is said. The other members of the group are not free to speak up or react at this point. The round gives people a chance to show themselves as they choose in that moment, with no reactions, except from the therapist. If something very important comes up during a round, I usually work with that issue immediately. It is like doing individual therapy in a group setting and may not necessarily involve a family constellation. In working during the round, I use any of the various therapeutic methods I have learned. On the one hand, the round serves as a preparation for later family constellations, since the individual participants become clearer about what is really important to them. On the other hand, it develops a deep sense of connection within the group. As the therapist works with one participant, all the others discover that they are also affected, and this experience has an effect on their own individual process. The "aha!" experience helps each person to identify their own situation and their own issues more clearly. It often happens that people's original issues change during this process. I remember a man who came to a group with the intention of working on his marriage. During the round, it became clear to him that he needed to clarify his relationship with his mother first.

I begin and end every seminar with a round. Sometimes, when the family constellation work during a seminar has been very intense, the participants also have a need to share their experiences. In a round, each has an opportunity to say what touches them or to add something, if appropriate.

The Family Constellation Process

Before I describe the process of a family constellation, I would like to say a word about this therapy method. A primary function of this work is to reveal systemic entanglements. Then, we can enter into the process of looking for resolution. In optimal cases, there may be a final step in which the entanglements are resolved.

Family constellations utilise a phenomenon that occurs when individuals take over a role in someone else's system. They have no specific information about the person they are representing, but still have reactions and feelings in that role. A clarification of the issue is the first step in a constellation. It is important for the client to remain very serious and present. A sense of seriousness reflects the client's motivation and sets the tone at a deep level. I place great importance on this seriousness, because my experience has shown that nothing can be changed if the client is proceeding from superficial curiosity alone. The same is true when someone is simply grasping at the last straw. If a client sees the family constellation as their last chance to be rescued from their crisis, it has a negative effect on the process of the constellation. Because of the pressures of the emergency, the client then often has some expectation that the therapist will provide relief.

Before a constellation, the client expresses in minimal words what the constellation is about and what the person hopes to gain. Sometimes this clarification turns out to be enough and no constellation is actually necessary because the client has already come to a clear decision. Once the issue is clear, the therapist and the client decide which persons are essential to this situation. The client chooses representatives for each person, including someone to represent himself or herself. The person who has brought the issue only takes his or her own place in the constellation near the end of the process. My experience has been that the client usually reacts with feelings and emotions, such as anger or grief, from outside the constellation. The change of perspective allows pain to surface and be felt in a way that is impossible when someone is inside their system and its entanglements.

The people involved in the situation are described only with facts. "My mother was married twice. She had a child in her first marriage that died at the age of two. My mother separated from her first husband. Her second husband is my father." Facts and the chronology of the family are what are important, including marriages, facts about children, or deaths in the family. The personal characteristics of these people are unimportant.

Representatives need only the bare facts. My impression is that a constellation works better when they have no additional information. The task of the representative is to remain sensitive and alert to what they actually experience in their roles. When they have been clearly instructed and understand that they are only to say what they actually physically feel, I can assume that their awareness in the role is a representation of the feelings of the actual persons they are representing. The client remains outside the constellation and can provide clarification or additional information if something more is needed by the therapist. As a therapist, I often get confirmation from a client's reactions to what happens in the constellation, such as, "Yes, that's exactly how my father always reacts!" If the representatives are personally affected and their own issues are touched upon, I can usually see that quite quickly and I replace them with other representatives.

The client's initial positioning of the representatives is of critical importance. Without any expectations of what will come, simply according to an inner sense of how things are, the client places each representative so that their relationships to one another are expressed. Relationships are indicated by the representatives' distance from one another and the direction they are facing in their positions. The client uses the representatives to set up an "inner picture" of his or her family, and the constellation acts as a mirror of this image. Various members of the same family will set up the family system differently, as each has a different sense of the relationships. The inner image of an elder brother will not be the same as his younger sister's, for example. In the course of the constellation, the therapist makes changes in the positions until it reaches the point that every representative is in a place that feels right. Interestingly enough, this feeling of rightness is dependent upon everyone in the system. I have often seen the opposite, an inner image in which everyone feels terrible.

In one constellation, a girl was standing between her parents, and all the representatives felt bad. They only felt better after the daughter had pulled back and the parents were able to stand next to each other. The daughter came to the group with an inner image of herself as the rescuer of her parents' marriage. During the constellation she discovered that her parents were better off without her intervention.

Not just in this case, but generally, children have nothing to do with the marital happiness or unhappiness of their parents and have to stay out of that issue.

With changes in the constellation, a new inner image emerges, with different effects. Troublesome inner images are usually based on early life experiences, and because they occurred at a young age, people hold on to them more firmly. If the pictures can be changed in a lasting way through a constellation, I often hear comments like, "My mother got a lot friendlier after the constellation, even though she wasn't there!" It isn't the mother who has changed, but the client's image. The relationship takes on a different value and meaning, and the client's behaviour towards his or her mother changes. That makes it possible for the mother to act differently as well.

I work on the basic therapeutic principle that relationships in a family are dictated by "primary love" and everyone feels better when each one can love all the others and take them just as they are.

There is a real danger in family constellations that people may use this form of therapy superficially. "I think I'll go and do a constellation of my family of origin." – "I guess I'll do a constellation of my present family now." Using constellations as the fad of the moment degrades a powerful method to a market product. Such an unserious attitude towards family constellations does not serve clients, but it does contribute to the unrealistic expectation that a constellation can somehow magically solve all problems. I inform all my clients at the beginning of a group that a constellation is nothing more and nothing less than a step in one's own development. I am fond of the image of a sailing boat changing its course by one degree and landing in a completely different place than originally intended. A constellation can contribute to a tiny course correction that may lead to a major change. As I have already said, the essence of this change rests in the inner stance and attitude of the client. A constellation is neither a miracle formula nor a magic trick and in no way guarantees that a problem will be solved permanently. I warn people that under certain circumstances they may even feel worse following a constellation, particularly if the work goes very deeply. This is due to loyalties within the family system that are stirred by any resolution of entanglements. The unconscious provokes a bad feeling and a guilty conscience in order to preserve unconscious loyalties, and it is important for clients to understand this connection.

The Dynamics of Family Constellations

No one knows exactly why family constellations work. I base my own explanation on certain hypotheses but mostly on my own experience. In a family constellation, something like an energy field seems to be established through the group participants and through the positioning of representatives. In each seminar group, there are twenty to thirty people, generally sitting in a circle to define the working space. Within this space a client places representatives who each take a particular role; one person represents the father, one the mother, and so on. Nonverbal communication is established based on how they are placed and the direction they are facing. The representatives feel this communication physically and can report their impressions. This communication is broken, for example, when a representative leaves the room and closes the door. It appears that the representatives are connected by some kind of energetic communication, which functions whether or not the people standing in the constellation know any factual information about their roles.

There is an exercise that I often do with my clients that demonstrates this nonverbal communication. I ask the members of the group to arrange themselves in pairs. They stand with one person in front and the other behind, without speaking. Then I ask them to pay attention to their physical sense and awareness. What does the person in front experience? What about the person standing behind? I ask them to identify how they feel; do they feel young or old, large or small, like a child or a parent, like partners or friends? Without a word being spoken, everyone has entered into a relationship with their partner in the exercise and each has feelings and associations that arise purely from the physical placement.

Another exercise is to ask group members to stand in pairs, facing their partner without speaking, and close their eyes. Still with their eyes closed, the two form a connection to one another and there are corresponding associations. One may feel like a mother, for example, and the other like a son, or they may feel like husband and wife. In this exercise I have noticed that the same people will have very different feelings and relationship associations depending on their actual physical position, whether it is one behind another, next to each other, or facing each other.

The client sets up a representation of an inner image of the tionships within the family. The representatives experience feelings and reactions in accordance with this image and placement. If the representatives are repositioned so that the picture changes, their feelings will also change. In real life, of course, it is impossible to change the actual positions of people in the system. In a constellation, our intention is not to manipulate the system, but to alter the inner image and attitude of the client. A person's behaviour may also change, of course, and the system will alter as a consequence.

One of the complexities of this process is that when one member of the system changes his or her image and behaviour, it affects all of the other members of the system. When I talk about images, I try to explain this process. It does not have to do with the individual alone, but rather with all of the inter-relationships and reciprocal effects within a system. These inner images are not created, but discovered, and a person's whole inner sense changes when a new image is discovered. The identifying characteristic of a newly discovered image is that it has impact and it brings about a feeling of resolution that is immediately visible in the client and the representatives. During the work, a therapist can very quickly determine the authenticity of the images that emerge. These images have clearly been of importance at some point in the client's life. They are not static images, but rather images that change over time.

If a client's inner sense has always been that his or her mother was unfair and unkind and preferred the client's brother, this inner image creates a sense of dissatisfaction and want that cannot be stilled by anything or anyone. If the client can say, "My mother gave me all she could, and what she gave is fine with me," it dissolves the person's demands and criticism towards the mother. It is clear that the mother's attitude towards the client will also change in some way.

"Happiness is being satisfied with what you have." This comment of Bert Hellinger sounds banal, but reaching this state of happiness is actually very difficult. The secret lies in gratefully accepting what I have been given and accepting that I have enough. When someone cultivates an attitude or feeling of not having enough, or not having received something at the right time, or not under the right conditions, it creates a constant feeling of not having got enough to ever be happy. In my experience, real satisfaction comes from deciding that what I have got is enough. This kind of decision can be supported through a family constellation.

The Role of Representatives

I would like to add something here about the role and experience of representatives. It is important to distinguish between the role in the constellation and one's own life. As a representative, I have found that no human emotion is foreign to me; I can feel anything when I am in a role. Nonetheless, it is important for representatives to be aware of their own identity, parallel to the role. At the same time, it is also possible to activate one's own awareness and developmental processes in a representative role. These three phenomena occur simultaneously: the role, your own identity and your own developmental process. Therefore, it may be useful to stay in the role for a while and allow the role to have after-effects. On the other hand, if the role is a very disturbing one, the representative should leave it behind quickly. A symbolic expression, such as leaving the room, shaking oneself physically, or washing one's hands, may be helpful in shaking off a role. It is the task of the therapist to recognise and deal with these phenomena.

Finding Resolution

It is easier to find a good resolution if we use the phenomena of bonds, order and a balance of taking and giving, as described by Bert Hellinger. A satisfactory resolution can usually be found if the therapist works with these basic principles of human relationships, but is also open to other phenomena that may arise. I need to emphasise that the resolutions found in family constellations are often contradictory to what the client is aware of and the situation as the person has described it.

A young couple, parents of a three-year-old child, came to a group. The woman was responsible for their participation in the group, as she wanted to know whether there was any chance for their relationship. If not, she was insistent that she retain custody of their child. She did not feel understood in the marital relationship and had fallen in love with another man. Because her child was very attached to her, she took it for granted that the child would have to remain with her in the event of a separation. For her, this was a demonstration of how much she loved her child. In a constellation, both partners discovered that it was not the wife who was misunderstood, but her husband. She had never really respected her husband as a husband, but had used (abused) him only as a provider, protector and substitute for her mother. This experience turned the world upside down for the woman. She had felt like a victim, and now she had to acknowledge that, as a result of her own entanglements, she had been unable to truly take her husband. This was uncomfortable for her—actually, quite a shock. As a result, she was able to resolve the entanglements in the system of her family of origin and it became possible for her to maintain a good relationship with her husband.

At this point I again want to emphasise that morals and social conventions play no role in finding a resolution. In the previous example of the young couple, if the resolution makes it possible for them to have a deeper and more loving relationship, the moral considerations play no part here.

Bert Hellinger goes so far as to say that an extra-marital affair should not be "confessed" or talked about and that kind of honesty usually has a negative effect on a marriage. If the second relationship is so powerful that the person has to leave the marriage, then it, of course, has to be discussed. A "fling" has very little to do with a person's partner and "confessing" shifts responsibility for the affair on to the uninvolved partner.

The basic phenomena of bonds, order and a balance of taking and giving are merely guidelines in a family constellation, and a therapist never knows in advance what the resolution will look like. The final image is dependent upon the experience and reactions of the representatives, and the therapist must accompany the process with an alert attention to whatever emerges. All of the feelings that the representatives report are taken into account in order to achieve the goal of the constellation. In an image of resolution, each family member represented feels respected and acknowledged in his or her position. What each has done for the others is respected and valued, beginning with the mother, who bore the child, and the father who has provided for the family, through to a possible inclusion of an earlier partner who was much loved.

I have noticed that in separations, the partner who leaves often tends to devalue his or her partner in an attempt to avoid feelings of guilt. The result is new feelings of guilt about having denigrated the former partner. In a family constellation, the person might say to the partner: "Thank you for your love. Thank you for all you have given me. I am sorry I couldn't give you more and I wish you all the best." In this way a relationship, even one that perhaps lies far back in the past, can be concluded in a positive way. Both partners are then free to enter into new relationships and to find happiness again.

Gratitude for a previous relationship is important. No one has a right to life-long love from another person. It is wonderful when it happens, but it is not always the case. People's demands on each other are often unrealistic. When the complaints of being misunderstood and badly treated continue to resound, even when the relationship is over, the pattern continues, and the bond to the partner remains. Honouring the love that was, and saying thank you releases the bond. Thank you, in this sense, reflects an inner attitude of a balance of taking and giving, it means, "I have taken, and I am now free again."

Sentences of Bonds and Sentences of Resolution

There are certain sentences that may be spoken in the course of a constellation that play an important part in finding a resolution. These sentences are always very simple and touch the person directly. They vary according to the situation and cannot be simply drawn from a recipe book. They have to match the individual situation precisely. A sentence of bonds expresses the dynamics of systemic relationships.

If a daughter has taken over her mother's suffering, the dynamics become clear with a sentence such as: "Out of love for you, I am carrying your pain." Sometimes just speaking this sentence aloud is enough to initiate a healing process.

The sentence of resolution in this case might be for the daughter to say to the representative of her mother, "Thank you for my life. I leave your pain with you." Acknowledging the bond by stating clearly that the suffering has been taken over from another out of love for that person is usually a path towards resolution. Speaking sentences that identify the systemic bonds make the dynamics of the system clear. Sentences of resolution resolve those dynamics. I sometimes break off a constellation after a sentence that identifies the bonds. This is the place to stop when the statement has stirred up strong feelings that were previously unconscious, or when someone is too overwhelmed by new information that has emerged.

It is tragic if a daughter is carrying her mother's sorrow because it helps neither the mother nor the daughter. The saying that "a burden shared is a burden halved" does not apply here. When a child takes on a parent's suffering, the pain is doubled because both are now suffering. Bert Hellinger is often asked about this phenomenon of one person taking on something from another. His explanation is that "everything and anything will be sacrificed for the sake of the bonds in family systems. One could call these bonds love."

Rituals of Resolution

These rituals support the process of resolution in the soul and are a physical expression of the movements of the soul.

1. Bowing down is the deepest expression of respect and at the same time an action that brings resolution. The more difficult it is for the client to acknowledge or agree to "what is", the deeper and longer the bow must be in the constellation. I differentiate four levels of expressing respect and humility, according to the degree of entanglement. The first, the weakest form, is a nod of the head. The second is a bow, bending the upper body while standing. The third is kneeling with a bowed upper body and the hands opened upwards as a gesture of letting go. The fourth level is the most powerful expression of humility, where the person stretches out fully on the floor. All of these rituals are carried out without speaking. As a rule they have a powerful effect and those involved feel very touched. Everyone can feel the healing power of allowing this deep acknowledgement to be expressed. The completion of this ritual often produces the sense of a burst of energy in the constellation.

2. When guilt feelings or other feelings have been taken over from another person, it may be useful to provide a heavy stone as a symbol of what has been taken over. I ask clients to put everything they have been carrying into this stone and when they are ready, then to attentively carry the stone to the person and give everything back. This may be accompanied by a sentence such as "I leave your suffering with you and take my life with gratitude." The client returns the stone to the other representative as a symbol of what has been taken over and carried.

The Role of The Therapist

Completely Present but Totally Removed

The first task of the therapist is to create a collected atmosphere and clarify the issue. The therapist and client work together to determine which people should be represented in the constellation. I give the client special instructions to ensure that he or she is fully collected before positioning the representatives. I place a high value on the serious nature of the placement. A lack of seriousness is revealed in questions such as, "Shall I position my mother as she is now, or as I experienced her when I was a child?" If the client seems to lack concentration or if the representatives are repeatedly moved around, it is a sign that the client is not collected and focussed.

When the representatives have been positioned, I move into the constellation, into the energetic field, with total awareness and then, again with full awareness, I move back out again. Moving into the field helps me to feel the next step and/or the resolving step. When I move back out of the field, I allow the whole to have its effect on me. During the constellation, I pay very close attention to the verbal and nonverbal reactions of the representatives in their roles: "I feel fine, here," "I feel superfluous", and so on, and representatives are moved according to their feedback. Bert Hellinger describes the state of the therapist during a constellation as "completely present but totally removed." To avoid bringing one's own projections, transference issues, or values into a constellation, it is essential to maintain a high degree of self-awareness. Social conventions play no role in a family constellation. What is important is only what strengthens and supports love.

Family constellations are always based on the basic principles of bonds, order and a balance of taking and giving. My primary question is, "Where has the natural flow of love been interrupted?" These fundamentals form a structure in the background from which I can always break away to follow new, individual phenomena. Being open to unexpected developments is just as important as the principles of bonds, order and a balance of giving and taking. In the process of the constellation, entanglements need to be presented and given space even though they are often tragic. When the entanglements are clear, we can develop steps towards resolution. Showing a client the entire process often touches such a familiar echo that the person is able accept and implement solutions.

When he first began doing family constellations, Bert Hellinger used to present the image of resolution without showing the whole process. In many cases, that had little effect. He then realised that the entire process of the entanglement and disentanglement had to be presented so that the client could feel the process in his or her soul.

During a constellation I continually ask myself what a possible resolution might look like, but that does not mean that I hold fast to any particular resolution. More usually, many possible resolutions appear in the course of a constellation, each of which can be tested out with the help of the representatives. If a client suspects that his or her mother had a relationship before the marriage, a representative is chosen for this man. The validity of the suspicion can be seen by the reactions of the representatives. It is essential to remain open to all possibilities in a constellation, and this is one of the things that make them so difficult.

When a client represses emotions to an extreme, I often become emotionally involved myself. It can get to the point where I begin to cry, when it is actually the client who should be crying. My tears are not tears of sympathy, but an expression of feelings taken over from the client, if that person is unable or unwilling to feel them. I have gradually learned to recognise this emotional reaction as a signal that there are repressed emotions.

I am often asked how I arrive at the sentences of resolution or sentences of bonds; perhaps it is purely intuitive. I believe the sentences arise out of a large resource of experience, gathered through years of practice and life experiences. But, there are also situations in constellations where I am stumped as a therapist. I may have the feeling that I can't continue and that there is no solution. In such a situation I have two choices. One avenue is to go with that feeling and state openly that I don't think there is a solution. Strangely, the moment I agree to my own limitations, a solution often appears. The second option is to wait. I wait and enter the field with awareness, moving between the important representatives. Inside the field I can feel the dynamics and sometimes a possible resolution becomes visible.

Transference in Finding Resolution

The phenomenon of transference was first described by Sigmund Freud as a transfer of feelings and behaviour to others that we had towards our parents. This phenomenon is primarily, but not only, evidenced with superiors and persons in a position of authority, including teachers, bosses, doctors and therapists. Of course this phenomenon also appears in family constellations. A client's anger towards a therapist often has its base in the original relationship with that person's mother or father. As a rule, children expect more from their mothers than from their fathers, and their demands for love, attention, and security are wants which are seldom satisfied. Therefore, clients have different transference issues with female "motherly" therapists than with male "fatherly" therapists. Fathers are more often identified as authority figures, and a client is more likely to accept suggestions, instructions, and recommendations.

I have found that the phenomenon of transference can be used as a resource in family constellations. A clear example of this is the case of Gitti (see p. **). In this case, the client's loyalty to her mother's fate made it virtually impossible for her to allow any feelings of anger to develop towards her mother. As the client responded to me, the therapist, with transference reactions that really belonged to her relationship with her mother, it was certainly possible for her to become angry and thus resolve a bit of the relationship with her mother. I was forced into the role of representing Gitti's mother when her feelings towards her mother were transferred to me as a "motherly" therapist. In this way, Gitti had an opportunity to find a resolution.

Transference occurs spontaneously and there are various ways of responding to it. During a family constellation, when I notice that a client is developing a mother-transference towards me, I suggest that a representative be chosen for the client's mother. This technique dissolves the transference and directs the client's feelings where they rightfully belong. Sometimes this course of action is not available, perhaps because the client does not want to let go of the transference. "That's not true! This doesn't have anything to do with my mother, it has to do with you!" In such cases I have to find a different way to deal with the issue. In Gitti's case, I allowed her anger to remain directed towards me, although I was quite certain that it had to do with her relationship with her mother. Since I took her anger seriously, Gitti had an opportunity to express her anger. In the end, even though it was based on transference, the effect was so positive that I could only recommend this approach to any therapist.

Working with Symptoms

Illness and Symptoms

Both as a physician and as a psychotherapist, my work is primarily with people who are ill. This leads to the question of how best to use family constellations specifically for the healing of illness and physical complaints. I have found that it may be useful to set up a representative in a constellation to symbolise an illness or physical symptoms. A representative is chosen to stand for the illness, such as a particular form of cancer. The role is abstract, so there is no reality for the representative other than what is actually felt in the role. Amazingly, representatives become aware of feelings and reactions, exactly as they would in any other role.

Symptoms Express Love

As I described in Chapter Four, patients are often able to find personal meaning in their illness or physical complaints. A positive interpretation for a susceptibility to chills might be, "I need to make more time for myself." To break the vicious circle of diarrhoea, it might be useful to try, "No time, no relief, always there for others," for example. A positive interpretation does not always work, and generally has limited value when the disorders are of a more serious nature. This expression of love is always unconscious, which is why a family constellation is a useful method of bringing it into awareness.

I often use a simple exercise called symbol trance, in which I ask patients to choose a symbol of their symptoms. If the symbol is a pleasant one, such as a meadow full of flowers, the client feels comfortable; the person feels good in his or her entanglements and with the symptoms or illness. In the therapeutic work, this is an indication that the love in the system may be stronger than the desire to recover good health. In many cases, simply the process of noticing the symbols is enough and a family constellation is not needed in order to find a resolution. If the symbol is threatening and anxiety producing, for example a skeleton, it is an indication that the patient is looking for a solution. In this case, it is important to make room for a loving response to the threat, which represents some unknown person or thing. I ask the client to look at the symbol and to "give it whatever it needs". In my experience, what is needed is always love and respect. If the patient is able to allow those feelings to develop, it is the first step towards healing.

If I acknowledge that symptoms are expressions of love, it allows for a more constructive approach to each case of suffering. It also engenders more compassionate love in the therapist.

Symptoms as Indicators of Resolution

There are two ways of putting symptoms into a constellation. The first is of a diagnostic nature, which reveals where a symptom "belongs". If you put the symptom into a constellation, the representative of the symptom will be able to say precisely where he or she feels best, where the "right" place is. This information can be very helpful in making a diagnosis, since it indicates where it might be useful to look next.

In addition, symptoms are indicators towards resolution. If the best resolution has been found in a constellation, the symptom will always say, "Now I am superfluous; they don't need me anymore. I can leave." Whenever a representative of symptoms has a response like this, I know we have found a good resolution.

I remember a client who had always suspected that his father was not his real father. He believed that his mother had taken a lover during the war and that he was the child of this lover. The secret was never spoken of and his mother denied the whole thing. In the constellation, the image corresponded to the son's suspicion. I first put the representative of the symptoms in the father's family, but there was no place where the representative had the feeling of being unnecessary. Then I put the symptom with the client's mother and added a representative for the "other man" to test out the son's hypothesis. The representative of the symptom said, "Now I can leave," so the resolution was clear.

On the basis of my experience with these kinds of constellations, I deviate from the classic practice of having the client position the representatives, and I often encourage representatives of symptoms to move about freely in the working space. The representatives only need to follow their own impulses and later, when they have found a new place in the constellation, I ask them about their experience. Representatives of symptoms and illness respond exactly like representatives of clearly defined roles such as father, mother or sibling. It is clear that symptoms only belong to the family system as long as they are needed.

The complaint may also be symptomatic behaviour. In the case of a man who came to a group because of a lack of professional success, it became clear that the man's father had also been unsuccessful in his career and had been scorned by his wife because of it. I set up a constellation of the father, the mother, the client, and the symptom of "lack of career success". When the son was able to honour and respect his father as father, the symptom no longer felt needed and was free to withdraw. The consequence was that the son was able to pursue success, since he no longer needed to avoid a successful career out of loyalty to his father.

When guilt has been taken over from another person, it sometimes happens that the representative of the symptom feels better lying next to the original victim. Then the client is free to leave the symptom there, at its origin. This situation might arise, for example, when there are war victims involved in the situation.

It sometimes becomes clear to me during a constellation that no resolution is possible at this particular point in time. Perhaps there is some loyalty that outweighs all other considerations, for example, loyalty to a grandfather. In that case the only option is to agree to the symptoms and say something to the loved one such as, "Out of love for you, I will remain depressed." In such a situation, I would recommend that the client imagine the grandfather every time symptoms of the illness reappear, and repeat, "Out of love for you, I will gladly carry this depression." This sentence alone may bring resolution and a relief of symptoms, but sometimes only after two or three years. I give such recommendations to clients much as I would prescribe medicine. For me, the effects are comparable to those of medication.

Symptoms and Secrets

There are secrets in every family, many of which can and should remain secrets, such as the parents' intimate relationship. But, there are certain secrets that a child has a right to know. A child should have access to everything that has to do with his or her origins. That includes knowing a biological father, even if he does not live in the family; for an adopted child it includes knowing the natural parents; in addition there may be information about half siblings and what has happened to them or about siblings who have died. Parents are responsible for telling their children about other siblings who were aborted, born dead or given up for adoption.

If either or both of the parents had important previous relationships before the child's birth, these also play a role. According to Bert Hellinger, children often represent previous partners of their parents; therefore, it is essential for them to know about these relationships.

Secrets in a family system should also be open to later generations in an appropriate way. Have there been any incidents of early deaths, violent deaths, crimes or very difficult turns of fate in earlier generations? How, and to what extent, the secrets should be uncovered depends on the fate of the following generations. For example, if a grandchild is suffering from serious depression, knowing about a secret from the past could be critical for resolution and healing in the sense of systemic dynamics.

While working in the hospital, I once got to know a pastoral assistant who was primarily involved in the pastoral care of terminally ill patients. I asked her what she was able to do with these patients who knew that they were dying. She said that she always asked them what they still had left that they wanted or needed to take care of. Very often there was a pressing need to reveal some secret about their life or family. It is clearly meaningful for dying people to be freed of the burden of carrying secrets, and they feel relieved when they have an opportunity to do so.

Secrets and Guilt

These days, we see many crimes from the Nazi era being uncovered and looked at. Many of the perpetrators have never spoken to their families about their actions or have only been able to offer some justification that might appear plausible.

Although the generation of perpetrators may have been unable to look at what happened, the children and grandchildren now want to know about the role of their forefathers. Loyalty to the system works against this kind of clearing, but not knowing very often leads to severe symptoms such as depression, sterility or anxiety. At some point in the family history, a desperate effort to remain ignorant slowly changes into a demand for knowledge. Bert Hellinger's work can be looked at in this context.

In family constellations, I often get to a point where it becomes clear that the client is burdened with guilt from a previous generation. Usually there are only vague hints of what happened, or perhaps a complete gap in the available information. Attempts to check into the past are difficult since those involved may already have died or may have "forgotten" everything.

When representatives react in a way that would indicate some guilt from the past, we can address that, but it is not always useful to try to expose the guilt. If the client is still very caught in loyalty to the system, uncovering any connections to guilt from the past may exacerbate the situation. Another danger in uncovering past guilt is that the descendents are tempted to judge and blame the guilty parties. That cannot be permitted.

The solution is always to respect the fate of those involved, including the fate of the guilty, and to leave the guilt with those who bore the responsibility. In constellations, bowing down is always one of the most important interventions. Bowing down is a sign of respect and honour, but also a sign of leaving the other to his or her fate.

Symptoms and Reconciliation

All of my therapeutic work rests on the principle of recognising symptoms as helpers and friends and using them in this way. I first became acquainted with this way of thinking in the reframing techniques of NLP (neuro-linguistic programming). Illness acts as a support for finding one's own way, for identifying one's own place in the system and agreeing to it. Battling against disease also fosters a bond with the disease. I would interpret this battle as an expression of holding on to unconscious entanglements, whereas only agreeing to an illness can resolve it. Therefore, it is useful to exchange the image of struggle for an image of reconciliation, accepting the illness as a central part of oneself and one's life. The same is true of dealing with death. One of my main tasks is communicating this approach to my patients.

Reconciliation is also possible in family constellations: reconciliation between victims and perpetrators, with illness and death, above all, with those things that we do not want to allow into our awareness. The orders of love, as Bert Hellinger has described them, allow us to take these critical steps towards reconciliation.

Movements of the Soul

Bert Hellinger has continued to develop his work with a process he calls "movements of the soul". In these constellations, reconciliation can occur without words, merely through the movements of the representatives. What is different about them is that the representatives are free to follow their own impulses and move in whatever way feels right within the space of the constellation. The movements of representatives appear to follow a basic principle of reconciliation.

> A 63-year-old man came to a seminar because of a problem with impotence. In a symbol trance, the symbol for his problem appeared as night. He chose a representative for himself and one for night and placed the two facing each other. I asked the representatives to move according to their own inner impulses. In the first movement, the man's representative embraced night until she pushed him away. He turned away and appeared to be in despair, with no sense of direction. After a while, he turned to night again and she stood with her arms open wide, looking at him in a friendly way. He bowed down before her, and then kneeled and remained motionless in this position. After a while he stood up and the two representatives stared at each other with some intensity. I left it at that.

"Movements of the soul" constellations take a lot of time, and the task of the therapist is to remain present and alert. I would like to look at the constellation described above in view of the background information provided by the client.

> The client's paternal grandmother was Jewish and had died during the birth of the client's father. The woman's sister then adopted the baby. This woman was killed in Auschwitz. It is probable that the night is a symbol for the deaths of the father's mother and aunt. In the constellation, their fate was honoured.

In working with movements of the soul, it is essential to refrain from further interpretations of the dynamics. I have very cautiously presented a limited interpretation here in order to make it more visible. In the actual case, only the symptom and the client were set up in the constellation. The following example shows the movements of the soul in a different constellation.

Elsa, aged 39, had suffered greatly from a lack of contact with her father. Her father left her mother when Elsa was four. Her grandmother was killed in a concentration camp.

The constellation consisted of Elsa and her grandmother. To begin with, they stood facing one another. Then, the grandmother slowly lay down on the floor and Elsa lay down next to her. She turned to her grandmother and embraced her lovingly. I brought in a representative for the father and placed him in front of the two on the floor. The father sat down alongside Elsa. She sat up and leaned against her father. They embraced and looked with reverence at the grandmother lying near them. The grandmother closed her eyes and lay quietly and completely relaxed. The image was one of peace and calm.

Without a single word it was clear that the grandmother could be at peace as soon as love was allowed to flow between her son and her granddaughter and when they could look at her with respect.

Four weeks later, in the next group, Elsa reported some important changes. Her father had made contact with her again after a long time and had spontaneously offered to give her his mother's letters to read. She was very happy and felt settled.

During the same week end another participant, Lore, talked about her father who had been in the SS during the war. Lore seemed untouched as she relayed this information, but Elsa had a very strong reaction. She felt nauseous and had to leave the room. In the next round after a break, Elsa reported a conversation she had had with Lore about her father. As she talked, Elsa appeared to feel very smugly superior and I suggested that we do a constellation.

Elsa chose a representative for her grandmother, and Lore chose a representative for her father. I placed the two representatives facing each other and asked them to follow their inner impulses. Very slowly and sensitively, the two moved towards each other, pulled away and moved close again. Finally, the SS man (Lore's father) bowed down slowly before the Jewish woman (Elsa's grandmother) and wept. The Jewish woman went to him and laid her hands on his head for a long time. Then she pulled back and the SS man stood up hesitantly. They looked at each other for a long time. We left the constellation like this.

The second example of a movement of the soul describes the process of reconciliation. On the one hand there is reconciliation within the individual family system, in the form of Elsa's reconciliation with her father and Jewish grandmother. On the other hand there is reconciliation between victims and perpetrators from two different family systems, as with Elsa's grandmother and Lore's father. This reconciliation works metaphorically for those involved, perhaps even in a larger context.

Family constellations are often concerned with entanglements with people who have already died. As a result, I often encounter the theme of reconciliation in working with issues from the past, as the two previous examples illustrate. Besides reconciling with the dead, reconciliation with the living is also important. In my experience, when reconciliation cannot be had in real life, it is only possible then at a higher level. It may mean the level of belonging to a family and their common fate. Through acknowledging this reality of belonging, it is possible to reach a higher level of experience. It is not simple to explain these transcendent areas, but they appear in family constellations, particularly in those that involve movements of the soul.

Bert Hellinger has said that the movements of the soul go far beyond our theories or ideas of good and evil. They show us how we are connected to larger movements that we participate in and in which we need to find our place.

Dealing Symbolically with Symptoms in Preparation for a Constellation of Symptom Representatives

It can be very useful to find symbols for symptoms and to work with the symbols therapeutically.

1. The symbol externalises the complaint, for example a brightly coloured ball might represent a headache. This means that the symptom is imagined as a coloured ball outside the body, which allows the client to relate to the symptom. This symbolisation can be done in several different ways: through drawings, through a family tree, through symptom trance, or by finding an actual, concrete symbol.
2. Symbolising the symptom allows us to work undercover, with direct access to the unconscious (see symptom trance). This makes it possible to work around conflicting loyalties at the conscious level, such as suffering taken over for another family member out of love.

Symptom Trance

The first step in this process demands an exact definition of the symptoms. It is important to understand the meaning of the symptoms for the client and the degree of suffering they cause. If the client suffers from many complaints, I work out with the person whether, and in what way, the symptoms are connected and how they might be serving each other.

With a body relaxation exercise, I guide the client into a trance state. In a kind of dream journey, I lead the person through meadows and woods until we come to a clearing in the woods. I ask them to find a quiet place there and think about their symptoms. At this point I tell them that the symptoms will appear as they cast their eyes over the clearing.

The symptoms almost always appear as a symbol: a figure, a person, a character from a fable or something abstract like a black hole. The point of this preparation is to be able to work with the symbol later. In the constellation, I can then put in a representative for the symbol.

> In the case of Andreas (aged 24, single with no children), his complaint was that he suffered from panic attacks. In a trance, he experienced his panic as a black hole. I chose a representative for the black hole and we set up this representative as well as a representative for Andreas. I asked the representatives to follow their inner impulses and find their own positions. They approached each other slowly and lovingly. When the symptom lay down on the floor, Andreas's representative lay down slowly and carefully next to him. Nonverbally, he asked for permission to get very close to the symptom representative. They embraced each other warmly. Andreas then stood up slowly, leaving the symptom representative lying relaxed on the floor with his eyes closed. When Andreas had taken in this peaceful image, he could turn and look into his future.
>
> Four weeks later, Andreas came to the group again. Beaming, he reported that he had not had any panic attacks. I never heard from him again.

Neither the client nor I knew where the symptoms came from or what entanglements may have been originally responsible. Bert Hellinger would perhaps say that the soul already knows what everything means. The unconscious reacted, and in this case it was not necessary to bring a resolution to the level of conscious awareness.

I have described how I use trance induction as a preparation for the actual constellation, but in some cases I have found that the trance alone can have a healing effect. To explain this phenomenon, I would like to return to the process of the trance. When the symptom has appeared, I ask the client to give the symptom whatever it needs, whatever will help. It is not necessary to explain in detail what the symptom might need. That is explained in the visualisation. Usually it is life, attention and care. I ask the client to allow all the changes to occur as if in a dream and to remain aware of them. At the end of the trance I ask them to bow to the symptom. The constellation occurs in the imagination, so to speak.

Actual Symbols for Symptoms

In a different way of working with symptoms, which I learned in NLP, I ask the client to go for a real walk and think about their symptoms. They should imagine that the symptoms are calling to them. As a memento, they might choose some symbol from the environment. It could be a stick, a leaf, a pinecone or an old rusty tin. Afterwards, the client is asked to carry this symbol and to handle it with care. The reason behind this assignment is to loosen the symptoms from their physical attachment and externalise them. Then, the client has a new way to relate to the symptoms, no longer viewing them as the enemy, but as friends, and can act accordingly.

> There was a 52-year-old man, married, with one son, who was suffering from psoriasis, a skin disorder. What stood out was the fact that the disease had got much worse after he became happily married. In trance he saw the symbol as a porcupine that wanted some attention from him. He took the assignment seriously and imagined the porcupine as his constant companion. The psoriasis disappeared, and the healing remained even after the porcupine faded from his imagination.

In this case, the entanglements that might have contributed to the disease are not clear. Nonetheless, working symbolically with the symptoms cured the disease.

> A couple had been married for thirty years and had two grown children. The husband found it difficult to remain faithful to his wife and repeatedly had affairs. The client called his symptoms (affairs) "fear of intimacy", but during the constellation it became clear that he had taken over this fear of intimacy from his wife. The man was shocked to discover that his symptoms, (which were regarded very critically by everyone, including himself) were actually an expression of love for his wife. The sentence of resolution was, "I trust that you can handle me. I am your

husband". I met the client again three months later and he told me that the constellation had had a good effect on their relationship.

This case is an illustration of how couples can take over feelings for one another.

The Meaning of Symptoms and Illness: Case Studies

The following case studies provide examples for us to use in looking at the meaning of symptoms and illness in family systems. With this particular focus in mind, extraneous details of the constellations have been omitted here. Limiting our observation also intensifies the essence of the constellation. I would like to point out that many of these constellations were preceded by years of psychotherapeutic work using various other methods and that work needs to be acknowledged. We can assume that in many cases this psychotherapeutic work is what allowed a resolution to appear quickly. At the same time, it is sometimes possible to find resolutions quickly without any long preparation beforehand. It is difficult for me to predict in advance how quickly a resolution can be found. My experience has been that serious illnesses such as cancer, or serious mental disturbances such as anorexia or depression, generally indicate weighty and difficult entanglements. Unfortunately, it is usually true that the deeper the entanglements, the longer the path to healing.

I am often asked why I have continued to work as a therapist past the normal age of retirement instead of enjoying my free time. There are two answers to that question. Firstly, I have always considered my childlessness to be a deficit. It pains me that I cannot pass on something existential in that way. Working with Hellinger's style of family constellations allows me to pass on my experience and my love. It is not a real substitute for having children, but still meaningful.

The other reason for my continued fascination with constellation work is the opportunity it provides to touch the essentials. Revealing the dynamics of entanglements and consequently the dynamics of the symptoms, acknowledging and agreeing to the way things actually are, and accepting the fullness of one's own life, are often only possible through a family constellation.

The following case studies are based on family constellations that I have led. They have been intentionally abbreviated, to draw attention to the essential aspects. The information about each family system is limited to what is absolutely necessary for understanding. Descriptions such as "the symptom feels superfluous" or "the father feels good", and so on, are not quoted verbatim, but are summaries of the whole situation. Following changes in the constellation through adding representatives or changing positions, I always ask what has changed for the representatives. The reactions are often spontaneous and nonverbal. All of these transitional phases are summarised here. When choosing representatives for symptoms, I always ask clients to consider carefully whether it should be a man or a woman.

1. Symptoms as an Expression of Loyalty

Loyalty to an Excluded or Disowned Person:

Heinz, Asthma and a Dead Uncle

Symptom: bronchial asthma

Present family: Heinz is 17 years old and the second of four children. Both parents are present during the constellation.

Constellation:

Heinz's mother sets up the constellation. She chooses representatives for her husband, for Heinz and for herself. The son's representative is looking outward. His father and mother stand at respective intervals behind him, looking at his back. The son's representative feels terrible. His mother feels an urge to follow him. His father experiences very little feeling.

I choose a representative for "asthma" and place this person facing Heinz. Heinz and his mother immediately feel better. Then I move the symptoms to a position behind the mother and turn Heinz towards her. The symptoms' representative confirms that this place feels exactly right. This confirmation from the representative indicates that the matter has something to do with the mother. I ask the Heinz's mother about any remarkable details about the members of her family.

She reports that her eldest brother died shortly after his birth, four years before she was born. I choose a representative for this brother and place him next to the mother.

The symptom representative reports feeling unnecessary and pulls back out of the field. The mother and her brother stand next to one another. They both feel very sad. Heinz is also feeling sad but can breathe more freely.

I ask the mother to take Heinz's hand and stand with him in front of her dead brother. She says to him, "This is my dead brother. He belongs to us. His death has nothing to do with you." I have Heinz and his mother both bow down to her dead brother, who looks at them in a friendly manner.

Two things pointed the way towards possible resolution in this constellation. The mother told us about her dead brother, and adding a representative for this brother resulted in the symptom's representative feeling unnecessary. Heinz's representative felt an immediate relief in his ability to breathe freely, which confirmed my suspicion that his asthma was a substitute for the unrecognised uncle. The second step towards resolution was Heinz and his mother bowing down before the dead family member and his friendly reaction.

Johann, Heart Pain and His Mother's Secret Lover

Symptom: heart pain

Present family: Johann is 50 years old, divorced, and has no children.

Constellation:

The constellation includes representatives for Johann, his father, his mother and his symptoms. The mother is turned away, facing outwards with a blank look on her face. I ask Johann, who is sitting outside the constellation, if anything remarkable happened in his mother's family. He says that his mother's father died young, so I choose a representative for this grandfather and place him facing his daughter, Johann's mother. She does not react and continues to stare out into space.

When asked again, Johann says that his mother once mentioned something about a Russian, but he didn't know any details. On the basis of this information, I choose a representative for this man and place him facing the mother. She looks at him briefly but looks away quickly as though looking at him were not allowed. It is only when the Russian's representative is asked to lie down in front of her that the mother moves slowly towards him, lies down next to him and embraces him lovingly. The symptom's representative continues to stand behind the prone Russian.

When the mother has lain in this embrace for a while, she says that she feels as if she has been awakened from the dead. The symptom takes a step backwards.

The mother and the Russian man stand up slowly and remain standing next to one another. I ask Johann to bow down to the Russian and then to look at his mother and tell her, "I respect your love for the enemy." This is very difficult for Johann to say. The symptom remains near the Russian man. When Johann's father has bowed down before the Russian lover, the symptom can move away.

The symptom of heart pain is an expression of love here, in many ways. One the one hand, it is an expression of the mother's love for her first lover and his love for her. The first decisive step in the constellation is that the love for a man from an enemy country is revealed. Johann was surely representing this first lover of his mother. For that reason, he was unable to find a satisfying relationship in his own life. The client was very aware of his close relationship with his mother and of course knew nothing about her Russian lover.

On the other hand, the symptom was an expression of loyalty towards his father. The symptom was able to withdraw only when the father had bowed down before his wife's Russian lover. Johann's heart pains were noticeably lessened in the days that followed.

Johann had sought help in therapy in connection with his failed marriage, but without success. On the contrary, his emotional difficulties found expression in heart pains. Previous family constellations had shown that his mother was tied to some kind of secret. In this case it was essential that her secret come to light. The mother's first love was an enemy, which meant that she needed particular protection.

Eva, Nausea, and Her Aborted Child

Symptom: nausea

Present family: Eva is 40 years old and married. She has a one-year-old son.

Constitution:

Constellation:
The constellation includes representatives for the symptom and for Eva. The symptom reports feeling fearful and wanting to run out the door. I place Eva and her symptom facing each other. They look at one another, but the symptom feels afraid and does not want to look at Eva.

Without being asked, Eva, sitting outside the constellation, says "I had an abortion." The symptom's representative feels relieved and now looks at Eva's representative lovingly. Eva embraces the symptom and in tears she says, "I am sorry." When she has made a place for her pain and experienced it for a while, she looks at the symptom and says, "Now you have a place in my heart."

In this constellation, the symptom stands for the aborted child. When Eva says that she has aborted a child, the symptom reacts very clearly. It was not necessary to add a representative for the aborted child. The resolution lay in allowing the pain and taking the aborted child into her heart.

Abortion always has an effect on the family system. Even a clear justification for an abortion does not alter the effects. The child is not allowed to be born, but still belongs to the family. In the hierarchy of siblings, that child has a place, albeit an invisible one. The mother carries the guilt for the abortion. The guilt can become conscious when the mother, as in the above constellation, is able to say from the depths of her heart, "I am sorry." The child is honoured and has a place in her heart. If this process does not occur, the abortion is forgotten as quickly as possible and repressed, with a negative effect on everyone concerned. This is reflected in this constellation of Eva. There may be different dynamics when both parents are involved in the decision to abort a child.

Loyalty to Biological Father

Christian, Loss of Energy and His Biological Father

Symptom: psychosomatic exhaustion

Present family: Christian is 49 years old and married for the second time. He has no children.

Family of origin: Christian was born in 1941 in Breslau. His father was a pilot who was reported missing in action in Stalingrad. His mother did not remarry and died in 1990. Christian has always had doubts whether his putative father was actually his biological father.

Symptom trance: The symbol that appeared for the symptoms in trance was a beggar.

Constellation:
The constellation includes Christian and the beggar. The beggar is standing behind Christian and lays his hands on Christian's shoul-

ders in a kindly manner. Christian experiences this as a burdensome weight. He turns to the beggar and drops to the floor. The beggar says, "Now I have lost contact with you."

I choose a representative for the father and place him next to the beggar. This produces no change for the representatives. I choose a representative for the mother and place her next to the beggar.

Christian stands up and spontaneously cries out, "There's something you owe me!" The mother sways. I move the beggar to a position behind the mother. She feels more stable. Since Christian has always questioned his paternity, I choose a representative for the mother's possible lover and put him to the right side of the mother. The father stands next to the mother on the left side and the beggar remains behind her.

The beggar says, "Now I am superfluous," and pulls back. There is a clear attraction between Christian and the lover. The mother's lover takes Christian in his arms and Christian begins to weep. I ask the mother to join her lover in holding Christian. Slowly he becomes calm again. The mother steps back and says, "I don't know what to do. I am so sorry."

Christian reacts with anger: "You have lied to me!" His mother turns away. Christian and his biological father continue to hold one another. Christian says, "I belong to you. I have always known it. This has to do with the world of men." His mother turns to him again and says, "I am so ashamed. I am sorry." Christian remains standing next to his biological father, his mother stands somewhat off to the side, looking at the two in a friendly way, and she says, "It's good like this."

The beggar was a symbol for the biological father. That was clear because he pulled back when the biological father was added to the constellation. Christian's symptom of psychosomatic exhaustion was an expression of his loyalty to his mother's secret lover, his father. Christian's mother also felt better in the constellation when her secret was revealed. Taking in the natural father always brings a strengthening of male energy. In my experience, a man can only fully realise his strength when he has taken in his father.

As in every constellation, the dynamics of the resolution have effects in the entire system, not only between the persons we are focussing on. In this case the mother felt bad as long as her secret was covered up. When it was revealed, she experienced great relief and looked kindly upon her son and his father.

Loyalty to a Difficult Fate

Erwin, Heart Attack, and His Uncle's Fate

Symptom: heart attack and panic attacks

Present family: Erwin is 52 years old and married for the second time. He has two grown children from his first marriage, but no children from the second.

Family of origin: Both parents died some years ago. Erwin's father had six brothers. His mother always kept a picture of one of the brothers on her desk.

Process: In individual therapy, I sometimes have clients set up their family system using empty chairs instead of representatives for the family members. The client then sits on each chair to experience the feelings of that family member. The advantage of this method is that the client actually slips into the role of each member of the family.

Just as in a normal family constellation, Erwin chooses a chair for his father, his mother, his uncle and himself. When he sits on the chair representing his uncle, Erwin experiences the same feelings of panic he has suffered since his heart attack. At this point I interrupt the constellation and ask Erwin to get more information about this uncle. His father's youngest brother is still living, and Erwin finds out from him that this uncle was critical of the Nazi regime and was forced to commit suicide. He lived for three days after his suicide attempt and apparently suffered extremely before he finally died.

As the next step, I choose another form of systemic therapy, a visualised constellation. This is a constellation that occurs only in the mind of the client. In this constellation, Erwin is able to acknowledge and honour his uncle. I recommend that he perform an additional ritual by establishing some kind of memorial to his uncle, photos, mementos, flowers, candles, whatever seems right to him. Erwin agrees to follow this recommendation and promises to go to this memorial as often as it feels right and bow down before it. In this way he can pay his respects to the difficult fate of his uncle, and the therapeutic intervention can continue to have an effect.

I would interpret Erwin's heart attack as an attempt to balance out the terrible fate of his uncle. In any case, if he had died from this heart attack it would have brought him close to his uncle. Since he survived the heart attack, his panic remained as a balance to the uncle's suffering and his fear of death. This case was also concerned with a kind of family secret. The uncle's picture stood on Erwin's mother's desk, but he was never spoken of, nor did Erwin ever ask about him. By bringing the secret out into the open, Erwin was able to honour the terrible fate of his uncle and thereby to heal his own symptoms. Three years later I got a card from Erwin in which he reported that his panic attacks had never returned.

Irene, Panic Attacks, and Her Father's Dead Comrades

Symptom: panic attacks.

Present family: Irene is 35 years old, divorced, with no children.

Family of origin: Irene's mother died in 1990 and her father is 75 years old and lives alone. Irene is the youngest of four siblings. The other siblings are all married with children.

Process: The course of therapy with this client extended over two and a half years. In the first constellation, including Irene, her father and her mother, it looked as though Irene might have had a different father. For this reason, I suggested a genetic test to determine paternity. Much to Irene's surprise and to mine, her father reacted very positively to this and seemed to welcome the suggestion. He had also had doubts about whether he was Irene's father, because Irene's mother had had a relationship with an Italian man around the time of Irene's conception. Unlike her siblings, Irene had black hair and a dark complexion.

The genetic test proved her father's paternity, and I was quite astounded at Irene's response of indifference. She read me the loving letter she had received from her father, but she seemed to be unhappy about the results.

We set up another constellation and tried to look at all the pertinent details. There were no results pertaining to her symptoms, and her panic attacks continued and even became worse.

This cast the whole therapy into question, but Irene trusted me and chose to continue in therapy. I explained to her that it is sometimes difficult to find the essential entanglements, especially when there are very strong loyalties. In the course of looking into her father's history, Irene reported that he had had appendicitis as a young soldier and had been airlifted out of Stalingrad. All his comrades who were left behind were killed. This was the critical information.

Constellation:

The constellation includes the symptom, Irene and her father. The symptom moves directly to the father and announces, "This is where I belong." I choose five representatives for the dead comrades and place them in a row in front of Irene and her father. I then ask the father to take Irene by the hand and show her all his comrades in arms, and tell her, "These are my fellow soldiers. They all had to die."

I have both Irene and her father bow down before the dead soldiers. The symptom feels superfluous and moves away. Finally I have Irene thank her father for giving her life. As she does this, the dead soldiers stand behind her father, looking at her in a friendly way. From this point on, Irene has not had any panic attacks.

At the beginning of her therapy, Irene was very tied to her mother. In her first constellation, it appeared that she was identified with her mother's secret desire for another man. This is why the reality check of genetic testing was a critical intervention. This put me on the right track, which was her unconscious loyalty to her consciously rejected father. This sounds paradoxical, but is quite common. The soul of a child connects unconsciously to a parent who is consciously rejected. The paternity test gave us certainty but not a solution. Resolution was only possible when the death of the soldiers had been honoured by Irene and her father, and the gift of life taken in. The gift of life had to be taken in by Irene, but also by her father. The panic attacks disappeared when the tragedy was balanced through honour and respect.

Sabine, Jealousy, and Her Mother

Symptom: jealousy of a previous partner

Present family: Sabine is 40 years old, single and childless. She has been in a new relationship for the past six months. Her new partner separated from his wife six years ago.

Family of origin: Sabine's mother was abused by Sabine's father. Despite repeated serious health problems, her mother remained with her husband.

Constellation:

The constellation includes Sabine, her new partner and his previous wife. It is quickly apparent that the previous wife plays no role in this. Sabine and her partner both feel that they are standing much too close to one another. When I add a representative for jealousy, Sabine's friend looks only at this new representative. I ask Sabine who the symptom could be, but get no answer.

I place the symptom behind Sabine and the representative feels fine there. I ask Sabine to turn around and look at the symptom. She does not want to look. I have her say to the symptom, "I agree," and to bow down. She says this sentence, bows down and turns around again. The symptom remains standing behind her and both Irene and the symptom say that it is good like that.

Her friend has been somewhat off to the side during this exchange, and he now moves in closer to Sabine. He stops when he is at a distance that feels comfortable for both of them and Sabine says to him, "Now I take you as a man." They both look radiant.

Sabine's jealousy served the function of hindering the relationship with her new partner. One could guess that Sabine remained loyal to her mother and her difficult fate by not allowing herself a good relationship. She would have unconsciously regarded a happy relationship as a betrayal of her mother. Sabine agreed to her symptoms and showed them respect. In doing so she was able to turn fully to her friend.

In this constellation I intentionally left it unspoken as to who or what the symptom was representing. The effect of the constellation showed that Sabine's soul understood what it was about. In this case it would have been a mistake to try for more interpretation.

Lilian, Underweight and Her Grandmother

Symptom: underweight and myoma

Present family: Lilian is 45 years old, single and childless.

Family of origin: Both of her parents are living and have been married for 45 years. Lilian was born when her mother was 19 years old. She has a younger sister.

Symbol: In the symptom trance the symptom appears as a gravestone.

Process: In the first round, the client formulates her issue as, "I want to dare to show myself." Lilian says that her father was an illegitimate child. His father was already married and so could not marry his mother. The father's mother, Lilian's grandmother, committed suicide.

I ask Lilian to introduce herself to her grandmother and say to her, "Out of love for you, I am doing what you did." The client laughs and says that makes her happy. We leave it like that for the first day of the seminar.

Constellation:
The next day we do a constellation of Lilian, her father and her mother. Lilian is facing away from her parents, looking in another direction. She seems to be looking into empty space. I add a representative facing Lilian for the paternal grandmother who committed suicide. They look at each other. The client's representative looks radiant. The father says that he feels comfortable now that the grandmother is there. The grandmother says she feels unstable and is swaying.

Next, I place the mother and father next to each other, which makes the grandmother feel happy. I have the client tell her grandmother, "I love you. I understand you. I am unstable like you." When Lilian has said that, the two embrace one another and the grandmother says that she now feels stable. Lilian's parents are touched and feel good.

Final round: On the last day of the seminar Lilian says that she now feels more solid, but her grandmother is still with her. I suggest that she hang pictures of her grandmother in her house and look at them lovingly.

Lilian was identified with her father's mother, who committed suicide. Her grandmother couldn't show herself because the grandfather was married to someone else. This was expressed in the feeling of instability described by Lilian and her grandmother during the constellation. Out of love for her grandmother, the client could not allow herself to live her life fully. Her underweight was an expression of this. The identification with her grandmother was revealed. The identification dissolved when space was made for the love and it could be expressed. In this case, the work during the round served as preparation for the family constellation later. The process was further supported by the suggestion in the final round that the client look at photos of her grandmother. Lilian's original issue of wanting to show herself could be addressed and the first steps initiated through resolving the identification.

Elfriede, Breast Cancer and Her Dead Brothers

Symptom: breast cancer

Present family: Elfriede is married with three grown children.

Family of origin: Her parents, who have been dead for many years, were only married once. The client was born in 1943. She had two elder brothers, one of whom was reportedly handicapped. Both the boys died as children. Their actual ages at the time of death and the causes of death are not known.

Constellation:

The constellation includes the symptoms (cancer), Elfriede and her parents. Elfriede's representative stands between her mother and her father, and all three are looking at the representative of the illness, who is standing with her back to them. Elfriede says she feels no connection to the illness. The mother feels threatened by the disease. I turn the symptoms around so the representative is looking at the father and mother and place Elfriede next to the illness.

At this time I choose two representatives for the two dead brothers and place them next to their mother. Both of the brothers' representatives feel drawn towards the illness. Elfriede leans against the representative of the symptoms and feels supported there. When I move the illness behind the two dead brothers, Elfriede can barely remain standing. I ask her to look at her brothers, and she puts her hands around her neck as if she were going to choke herself. The mother is also reluctant to look at the boys, and she remains untouched.

When I have Elfriede tell her handicapped brother, "Dear brother, I love you. You belong here," he feels a sense of relief, and the illness pulls back a bit. Then I ask Elfriede to bow down to her brother. The representative of the symptoms reports feeling weaker and spontaneously moves back a few steps.

The client, who has been sitting in the group watching the constellation, seems untouched by what is happening. When I ask her to take the place of her representative in the constellation and bow down before her dead brothers, she refuses. The illness representative reports feeling stronger and moves nearer to the dead brothers. I end the constellation at this point.

Out of love and loyalty to her mother, Elfriede has taken over her mother's refusal to look at the dead boys. Her illness offers one way to follow her brothers into death.

Since the client showed no feelings during the entire constellation and refused to bow down to her dead brothers, one could assume that she will accept her death as a balance for the awful fate of her brothers.

Just as illness is sometimes incurable and leads to death, loyalties to a family system sometimes cannot be resolved. In such a case it is important to see this loyalty clearly and agree to it. If one can see the dynamics and feel the love that lies behind such loyalty, it is easier to agree to "what is". Elfriede stood before her brothers in the constellation and could not bow before them. Consequently, the illness regained its strength. Because I stopped the constellation at this point, the process that had become visible could go on working internally and have an effect.

Lisa, Her Depression and The Dead

Symptoms: depression with repeated suicide attempts

Present family: Lisa is 36 years old and has been married for four years. Despite her desire to have children, she has not yet conceived.

Family of origin: Lisa's parents divorced when she was twenty. Her maternal grandfather died on the day Lisa was born. When I asked what her grandfather had done in the Second World War, Lisa did not know.

Process: Lisa has had a lot of psychotherapy without any appreciable improvement in her condition. When it is her turn to speak in the round, she weeps and reports feeling angry and helpless. I notice a movement in her legs and suggest that she follow whatever the impulse is. She stands up and marches around the room. When I ask her who walks like that, she replies, "Soldiers."

Constellation:

The constellation consists of two representatives, Lisa and her depression. Depression is standing behind Lisa and reports feeling good. Lisa says, "It is pulling me down and away." Although I have no information, I bring in a number of representatives for the dead and have them lie down in front of Lisa and her depression. Lisa says, "It gives me goose bumps, but I can see clearly now." The representative for the depression breathes heavily and lies down with the dead. She immediately feels better lying there. She says that contact with the dead is pleasant. Lisa also feels better and reports feeling calm and clear.

I have Lisa take the place of her representative in the constellation. She looks away and is emotionally completely uninvolved. I end the constellation.

It is clear that the reactions of the representative do not touch anything in Lisa. Looking away is an expression of her loyalty. It is difficult to predict whether this loyalty will find some resolution in the future. In the immediate situation, the constellation cannot provide resolution, but shows a possible path that might be explored.

Loyalty to Secrets

Gitti, Lymph Node Cancer and Her Mother's Secret
Symptoms: cancerous tumour of the lymph nodes, with recurrence

Present family: Gitti is 32 years old and has been married for eight years. She has a four-year-old daughter.

Family of origin: Gitti's mother is 63 years old and healthy. Her father died of an acute heart attack at age 60 while Gitti was in hospital receiving chemotherapy. She has two younger sisters. One is anorexic and the other is bulimic.

Process: This therapy process continued over a period of three years. In the first constellation of her family of origin, it was clear that she had taken over something terrible from her mother's family system. Although she looked into the matter and asked questions, she was unable to explain what this secret might be.

After the first constellation, Gitti came up to me during the break and asked, "Is it really terrible if I want to die?" Surprised, I asked, "Who am I that you ask me such a thing? Someone else is responsible for that." She interpreted that conversation as agreement with her death wish.

Much later, Gitti told me that that experience had given her trust in me and made it possible for her to continue working on her illness using constellations. Since she was an art therapist herself, she decided to do a training course in family constellations. Working on oneself is a major part of this training so, over the next three years, Gitti had many opportunities to look at and experience the connections to her mother's family system from various perspectives. It was clear in each constellation that the solution would be to leave her mother to her fate and all that it entailed. That was impossible because of this deadly loyalty, in the most literal sense of the word.

When Gitti learned that her routine examination had shown signs of a recurrence of her disease, I suggested that she set up a constellation of herself and death. Her representative wanted to get closer to death, but the representative of death did not want to be near Gitti. She said to Gitti, "Live. Eventually you'll get here anyway. I can wait."

I had the feeling that Gitti was not able to take in what was happening and I broke off the constellation. She became very angry, particularly with me, and her anger had a remarkable effect. When she came to the next training group, she let out her rage in front of the entire group. Everyone in the group knew about her potentially fatal illness and they all listened to her attentively and with good will. Gitti expressed her anger with a strength that she had never shown before, and it was clear that in this expression of rage that Gitti had chosen life. No one said a word about any of this.

Effects: From that moment on, Gitti was a changed person. She seemed livelier and more powerful. That was two and a half years ago, and she has had no recurrence of her illness in that time. Following this decisive step, Gitti participated in another constellation in which she humbly and thankfully accepted life from her mother. She was able to leave the secret of her mother's family system with her mother.

In a constellation of her present family, she realised that she had taken over too much responsibility, not only for her mother, but also for her husband. This experience led to a marked improvement in her relationship with her husband.

The first step towards resolution was the therapist's agreement to the client's death wish. The second step was the client's anger towards her mother, which was transferred on to the therapist. The third step towards resolution, in which she was able to leave the secret with her mother, was only possible after this powerful expression of rage. In her loyalty to the terrible secret in her mother's system and as a balance for something which she would never even know, Gitti was prepared to die with the help of her illness.

Karin, Her Persecution Complex and Her Dead Aunt

Symptoms: persecution complex, which is described as a "shadow".

Present Family: Karin is 45 years old, divorced and has no children. She has had two abortions. When she was 16, she entered into a sado-masochistic relationship with a man thirty years her senior and she was a slave to him. This relationship lasted for twenty years and ended with the death of the married man. She was then married for only two years. Regarding the abortions, she said that she had been forced into it and didn't know why she had done it.

Family of origin: Karin's mother is 82 years old and lives alone in her hometown. Her father died twenty years ago. Her maternal grand-father was a man feared by all. Her mother's sister was said to have poisoned herself. The family suspects that the aunt was pregnant by the grandfather and that he perhaps gave her the poison that she used to kill herself.

Constellation:

The constellation includes Karin, her mother and the symptoms (the shadow). The symptoms' representative stands behind the mother and Karin is turned away. I move Karin to face her mother. The mother reports feeling cold and a deep void, but her back feels warm. This is where the shadow is standing. I move the mother and the shadow to face one another. The mother laughs oddly and says; "Now I'm freezing everywhere." The shadow's representative also reports feeling colder.

I turn the mother and the shadow so that they are facing out of the constellation. I put a representative for the dead aunt next to the mother. Karin stands behind this row, looking at their backs. The mother says, "I feel a heaviness and I have pains in my feet." The symptom says, "My hips are tingly and my hands are ice cold." Karin reports a feeling of wanting to run away.

I bring in a representative for the grandfather and place him next to the mother. She says, "The heaviness is letting up, it's getting lighter." The dead sister starts to cry and says that she feels terribly fearful. I ask the representatives to lie down on the floor in a very specific order. First comes the grandfather, next to him is the symptom, then the mother, and finally the dead aunt.

I move Karin opposite the prone representatives.

Mother: "I feel nauseous."
Grandfather: "I feel fidgety."
Dead Aunt: "I'm calm."
Symptom: "This is right."
Karin is confused. "There are a lot of unanswered questions."
I ask her to bow to all of them. Karin bows and then straightens up slowly. I place her opposite her mother and have her say, "Mother, I respect your fate and I will make something of my life."
Mother: "I am happy."

The dead aunt stands up spontaneously and embraces Karin warmly. She says, "Your love makes me feel good. I hope things go well for you."

When the dead aunt is lying on the floor again, I ask Karin to kneel down before them all. She feels some sense of relief when she has done this. She straightens up, and I add a representative for her father behind her. Karin becomes even calmer and says, "That feels good. Now I can look at these terrible things more calmly."

Karin's masochistic relationship to a man thirty years older than she could be a balance for the terrible fate of her aunt and also loyalty to her aunt's fate. It is not clear how entangled the mother was. The symptom felt that the place between the mother and the grandfather was the right place. That would indicate some entanglement between the mother and the grandfather.

After this first group, Karin felt much better. The symptom of the shadow was less torturous although it was still there. That concurs with the constellation in which the symptom remained between the grandfather and the mother. In this case the symptom could not withdraw. When a symptom representative can pull away or feels superfluous, that is an indication of resolution. In this case it is clear that although a first step has been taken, we have not yet found a resolution.

Anton, Deafness in One Ear and the Secret

Symptoms: deafness in the left ear

Present family: Anton is 50 years old and married with three daughters. His only son was hit by a car and killed at the age of five.

Process: Anton was the last person in a group to ask to do a constellation. In view of the fates of others in the group, he felt his own issue was too minor to warrant a constellation. In talking with him, it became apparent that he had difficulty saying either yes or no. Together, we decided to name his symptom of deafness in his left ear "yes-and-no".

Constellation:

Anton sets up representatives for himself and his symptom. He places the representatives next to one another, facing the same direction. Anton's representative says, "I feel rigid and I'm shaking." The symptom says that his right arm is trembling.

I ask Anton, who is watching the constellation, "Where are the two looking? Since they are both looking in the same direction, can they see something there?" Anton does not answer. I should have ended the constellation right there.

Instead, I move Anton and the symptom so that they are facing each other. The symptom pulls back and says he has got goose flesh. Anton moves towards the symptom again. The symptom trembles even more and Anton reports feeling full of energy. I ask the symptom to move nearer to Anton. Anton then says that he feels dizzy. The symptom trembles more strongly and wants to move out of this situation. I ask Anton to kneel down in front of the symptom, which he refuses to do. With a bit of convincing he finally kneels down. As soon as he does so, the symptom feels calmer. As Anton kneels, he begins to breathe heavily and his entire body begins shaking. He screams, "This sucks!"

I encourage Anton's representative to follow his impulse. He hides his head in his arms and turns away. The symptom says that he feels quieter and calmer. I ask Anton, the client, once again if there is anything particularly difficult in his family. He denies this. I end the constellation there.

I ask Anton how he is doing and his answer is, "I don't believe the representatives."

My response is "I can't do anything about this."

My error with this client was setting up a constellation in the first place. When it became clear that the client was unwilling to open himself to the constellation emotionally, I should have broken it off. I have deliberately included this case to make it clear that therapeutic efforts will not bring a resolution if the soul of the client is not ready.

Susanne, Her Heart Defect and Her Mother's Secret

Symptoms: serious congenital heart defect

Present family: Susanne is 47 years old and divorced. She has no children.

Process: Susanne did her first constellation because she wanted to decide if she should have another operation or not. It emerged in the constellation that there was some hidden secret in her mother's system and that Susanne's illness stood in direct relationship to this secret. It was clear in the constellation that she was prepared to continue carrying this illness out of love for her mother. I had to leave it at that.

After a year and a half, she came to another seminar, stating, "I want to live, now." Following the first constellation, she had had an operation, but not by choice. She had suffered a total collapse and had an emergency operation. Even then, she had delayed seeking medical help until she was almost dead. The operation was successful.

During the rounds she said over and over that she felt weak and tired. It was only on the last day of the seminar that she felt prepared to do a constellation. I felt a plea from her, almost a cry for help. When I suggested that she set up a constellation of herself and death, she agreed.

Constellation:
The constellation consists of Susanne and Death. It seems like she does not take death very seriously. I add a representative for Life. This representative feels terrible and stands with her head hanging. Only when Susanne can bow deeply before death is the representative for life able to pick up her head. She says, "Now I can look at you in a friendly way."

This constellation shows impressively how close life and death are. Only when death was honoured was life able to live.

Symptoms as an Expression of Guilt Taken Over from Another

Karla, Her Fear of Death and Her Grandfather's Victims

Symptoms: panic attacks and a fear of death

Present family: Karla is 24 years old and lives with her boyfriend in a shared flat.

Family of origin: Karla's father is the third of six children. Her grandfather was active in the Second World War, but his position and function is not known. He left his family two years after the war ended. Karla's father was four years old when his father disappeared "in the middle of the night". He never showed up again. When the grandfather was spoken of, he was referred to as "the black devil".

Karla is the eldest of three siblings. One sister is mentally handicapped.

Constellation:

The constellation consists of two female representatives, one for Karla and one for the symptoms. Karla and the symptoms stand at right angles to each other. Karla feels ambivalent about the symptoms.

I choose a representative for her grandfather (the black devil) and place him opposite Karla and the symptoms. Both Karla and the symptoms feel very strongly drawn to the grandfather. In various positions in the constellation, the grandfather states that he feels hard and cold.

I choose two women and two men to represent the victims of the grandfather (based on an assumption that there were victims). I ask the representatives to lie in a row on the floor in front of the grandfather. Only the female victims react with fear.

Therefore, I choose two more women representatives and place all the female victims in a circle around the grandfather. He stands up straight and says proudly, "I am powerful."

During this time, the symptom representative feels relaxed. Karla stands next to her father and looks at the grandfather's victims from a distance. She feels good standing next to her father. The father refuses to look.

Then, I open up the circle of victims and place them in a row behind the grandfather. The grandfather is now standing facing Karla and her father. I ask the grandfather to tell them, "It is my guilt. I carry the consequences."

He says this without any feeling or sign of regret. Karla shows no visible reaction. I choose a representative for the grandfather's guilt to stand with the grandfather. I have the victims again encircle the grandfather and the guilt. The grandfather begins to weep on the shoulder of his guilt. When his emotion is clear, the victims become calm.

I ask Karla and her father to bow deeply before the circle of victims. When they have stood up again, I open up the circle of victims and place the victims behind the grandfather and his guilt. The grandfather now says, "I am sad." When the grandfather shows his feelings, the symptom representative and the guilt representative both feel superfluous and pull back. Karla embraces her father and turns away with him.

Karla's symptoms are a balance to the guilt of her grandfather, who very likely left his home to keep his deeds from being discovered. Even the father was afraid to look at his father's guilt. This appears to be the origin of Karla's symptom. Unconsciously, she balances out the guilt towards the female victims with her panic attacks.

The resolution lies in honouring the victims and the perpetrator. Hand in hand with her father, Karla looks at the victims and her grandfather's guilt. By bowing in respect, the guilt is left with the perpetrator.

In the following days of the seminar, Karla's panic attacks became worse. As she gradually came to an understanding that her symptoms were an expression of her loyalty to her grandfather and his victims, her symptoms slowly improved, but it took some months.

In this case, perhaps it would have been more sensible to end the constellation at an earlier point, when the grandfather was moved to cry on the shoulder of the representative of his guilt. The exacerbation of the symptoms could be seen as an indication that Karla's soul was not yet ready for the resolution.

Bert Hellinger says in such cases, "The dead and the victims do not ask for any atonement. They want only respect and acknowledgement. Respect is what heals."

Theresa, Exhaustion and Her Father's Victims

Symptoms: psycho-vegetative exhaustion

Present family: Theresa is 58 years old and is married She has two children and four grandchildren.

Symptom trance: In trance, a huge dinosaur-like beast appears and puts its forelegs on Theresa's shoulders. When asked what it wants, it replies that it wants to be seen. That proves impossible, and it also turns out to be impossible for Theresa to bow down to the creature. When the reptile is resting on her shoulders, not only does she feel no fear, she feels quite comfortable.

Constellation:

There are two representatives in the constellation, one for Theresa and one for the symptom. They stand facing one another. The symptom says, "I'm curious about you." Theresa draws back. I ask her to move in nearer and she spontaneously falls to her knees. She feels better, but the symptom remains untouched. I add representatives for her father and mother. The symptom quickly finds a good place behind the father. When asked about her father's activity during the war, Theresa reports that he was classified as essential to the war effort and was not drafted. As the owner of a large paper mill he employed forced labour.

On the basis of this information, I add representatives for the victims and have them form a circle. The father and the symptom stand in the middle of the circle, but both feel unaffected by the configuration. The father is only interested in Theresa. Therefore, I ask the victims, the symptom and the father to lie on the floor. The symptom and the father lie next to each other. I choose an additional representative for guilt and place him on the other side of the father. The symptom feels superfluous and pulls away. The representative of guilt feels very uncomfortable in relationship to the father but feels connected to the victims.

I ask Theresa to bow down to those lying on the floor, but this brings no sense of resolution. I move the representative for guilt to a position standing behind those lying on the floor. The victims feel better, but the father continues to feel uncomfortable. Theresa feels some sadness. I ask the client to take her representative's place in the constellation and to kneel before the representatives prone on the floor. The representative for guilt says, "The gesture is right but the feelings aren't right." I end the constellation at this point.

The symptoms of psycho-vegetative exhaustion are an expression of the guilt taken over from her father. That is clear in the symptom's reaction to the guilt. When the guilt representative was placed next to the father, the symptom representative felt superfluous and could withdraw.

It was impossible for Theresa to let in any awareness of her father's guilt and, therefore, to honour his victims, so there was no resolution in the constellation. At this point, the essential entanglements were visible. Breaking off the constellation was necessary in order to allow this clarity to have an effect. It took two more years before Theresa was able to recognise her father's guilt and honour his victims. The most difficult part of the work for the client is to release the entanglement of guilt that has been taken over from someone else.

In the case of Karla, she saw the resolution and felt a sense of strength when it was found. Even so, she fell back into the old pattern and the symptoms recurred. In Theresa's case, she was unable to see the guilt because of her loyalty to her father. In order to allow in awareness of the guilt she would have had to give up her unconscious loyalty to her father and her illness as the unconscious atonement for his guilt.

In these situations the client is always fearful of losing the love of the person they are sacrificing for. This is a fear based on the fact that absolute loyalty ensures belonging and, therefore, love.

Theresa was not sure enough of her father's love to be willing to risk it. As in many cases, it is unimaginable to the soul of a child that the beloved father has been guilty of something bad. A child always wants a perfect father. Part of growing up involves giving up the idealisation of the father and seeing him as he really is, in this case, including his guilt. The resolution lies in thanking the father for life and for all that he has done and leaving his guilt for him to carry.

The sentence of resolution, "I leave the guilt with you," is almost always accepted by representatives of perpetrators. They usually react with relief and feel calmer. Often they report a feeling of peace. I interpret these reactions to mean that the perpetrators are also freed when they can finally own their guilt.

Anke, Her Compulsions and Her Father's Guilt

Symptoms: compulsions to wash and compulsive checking

Present family: Anke is 47 years old and is divorced by her own choice. She has three children who live with their father. She has a good relationship with her ex-husband and children. She states that her ex-husband still loves her.

Anke has suffered from various compulsive disorders ever since she was ten years old and her maternal grandmother died. Her compulsions have included washing, checking and a refusal to eat. She has made three suicide attempts, and for the past thirty years she has spent some weeks every year in psychiatric treatment.

Family of origin: Her father is 74 and lives with a female companion. Her mother died at age 55 when Theresa was 31 and had already had two children.

Process: Anke says in the first round, "I have to fight against my illness every day just for survival." My spontaneous reaction is, "As long as you are fighting against the illness, you won't be able to resolve this. The first step is to give your symptoms some room. They are an expression of your love for someone in your system." Anke seems confused and clearly does not know what to do with my comments. When asked about her family of origin, Anke reports that she can't seem to get free of her father, but she knows of no special circumstances in his past.

First constellation

The constellation begins with representatives for Anke and her symptoms. The illness takes hold of Anke's neck from behind and shakes her back and forth. Anke says, "I feel completely trapped." This is exactly how I have experienced the client, Anke, in the group, just as trapped as her representative in the constellation.

I add representatives for Anke's father, her mother and her father's parents and experiment with various positions for them. There is no apparent resolution, and it is unclear even which direction to go. What is most discernable is the strong bond between Anke and her symptoms.

Since this powerful connection is standing in the way of resolution, I break the constellation off and tell Anke, "It would appear that you are willing to go on suffering from these symptoms. The question is only, for whom?"

I give Anke the assignment to take some time during the break and find a symbol for her illness. After the break she returns with a twig, which she puts down carelessly somewhere. She tells us that during the search for a symbol she became very sad. I respond, "That must feel good." Anke says that she wanted to bring something in bloom. I tell her, "It is important for you to find some love for these symptoms. It is important for you to take care of them and stop fighting against them." Anke becomes very sad and starts crying. She says she doesn't want to do any more. I tell her that it would be a pity, and that I would be happy if she could stay.

I give Anke another task to write down everything that she has unsuccessfully tried to deal with her illness. She is annoyed but agrees. On the following day she comes into the group beaming and declares that she would like to bow down to her father.

Second constellation:
Without any further discussion, Anke sets up a constellation with representatives for herself and her father, facing each other. Anke says, "Let me go," and her father replies, "I can let you go."

I ask Anke's representative to enact Anke's wish and bow down to her father. She begins trembling, straightens up and leans forward against her father. As her shaking increases she says, "Please embrace me as your daughter." When he does so, her trembling becomes even more extreme. I ask Anke, the client, if something had happened with her father. She answers evasively, "There are pictures that come up ..." I tell her that it is not necessary for her to say it explicitly, and I choose a representative of a hypothetical guilt for her father.

The guilt stands behind her father. Anke's representative immediately feels calm. She leans back and says; "Now I can stand on my own two feet." I suggest a sentence of resolution for her to say. "You remain my father and I leave everything else with you." Anke says the sentence and smiles. Then, she turns away and her father remains standing with the guilt at some distance. Anke says, "Now there is space," and her father says, "Now I can breathe." The constellation ends here.

Process: The following day, Anke came into the group with the twig she had chosen as a symbol of her illness. She had put it in a vase and delicate leaves began sprouting from the twig. She told us that the previous evening she had eaten more and with more enjoyment than she had in a long time. Three months later I received a card from Anke in which she reported that she had gained five kilograms and was feeling well. She was not experiencing any compulsions and sent her thanks.

Although the father's guilt remained unclear, the constellation brought a resolution. After thirty years of therapy, and considering the severity of the illness, this had not seemed imaginable. The first step towards resolution was a loving approach to the symptoms as expressions of a binding love. The second step was a paradoxical description of everything that she had tried without success up to that point. The third step came from Anke herself in her wish to separate from her father, and this step brought resolution.

I have seen repeatedly that it is not always necessary to uncover secrets. On the contrary, when some secrets remain in the dark the intimacy of the system is protected.

At this point I would like to emphasise my conviction that illness and disease often carry some meaning within a system. This attitude allows for reconciliation with the illness. In Anke's case that meant giving up the battle against the illness. Since I am confident that these connections exist, I can make space for the client's healing capabilities. In the end, it was Anke's idea of bowing down before her father that brought resolution.

Marion, Her Toothache and Her Disowned Dead Brother

Symptoms: unbearable, recurrent toothache

Present family: Marion is 32 years old and single. She has a six-year-old daughter. She has contact with the father of her daughter, but says she can only stand to be near him in small doses.

Family of origin: Marion's parents are alive. Her mother was in a serious relationship prior to her marriage to Marion's father. The only thing Marion knows about that relationship is that her mother has a ring from that man that she guards jealously. Although she has tried to find about the relationship, Marion has not been given any information in response to her questions.

Process: In the first round Marion states that although she would like to marry the father of her daughter, she simply cannot bring herself to do it.

Constellation:

The constellation has two representatives, Marion and her symptoms (toothache). The representative of the symptoms stands behind Marion with an arm around her and reports feeling good in that position. Marion snuggles up against the representative and looks off into the distance. She reports that this position feels good to her, too. When I ask the client, Marion, for her reaction to this, she says that she has always believed that she has an older brother. I add a representative for this brother and place him facing Marion and her symptoms. The symptom moves away somewhat until Marion is standing in the middle between these two representatives. I move the "brother" nearer to Marion and both feel better. The symptoms move further away but remain in their field of vision. In this case, this means that the symptoms have something to do with the suspected brother, but there is also more that wants explaining. I add a representative for Marion's mother and place her in the original position of the symptoms, behind Marion. The putative brother feels fearful and wants to run away. The mother, too, is displeased and wants this "brother" to disappear. The brother sits down on the floor, and Marion sits down next to him. They embrace warmly. The mother looks at the two of them and says she feels sick.

I put a representative for the mother's previous partner next to the brother. At this moment, the symptoms' representative says, "I feel superfluous." I ask Marion to say to her mother, "I gladly atone for your guilt." When the representative says this sentence, she experiences terrible toothache. The mother turns away. I bring in a representative for Marion's father and place him next to Marion. They both say they feel fine in this position. I put the alleged brother next to the mother's previous partner and they both report that it feels like a good place for them. The mother remains turned away and says, "It's best for me this way."

Marion has felt unable to take the step to marry the father of her daughter. In this way she is following her mother, who could not take her first partner, although we do not know why that was so. More information came from the reactions of the representatives in the constellation. With Marion's statement of bonding to her mother, "I gladly atone for your guilt," the representative felt the symptoms of toothache. The pain disappeared when Marion's father was placed next to her, and her mother turned away. The resolution in this constellation lay in the final image. Each of the children stood next to their fathers and the mother turned away from the others. This would indicate that the mother is still bound in some way to her system of origin. When Marion could agree to this image, she was free to live her own life.

Symptoms as an Expression of One's Own Guilt

Hedwig, Her Pain and Her Betrayed Partner

Symptoms: constant pain in her left arm that has proven resistant to all therapeutic intervention

Present family: Hedwig is 60 years old. She has never been married and has no children.

Constellation:

The constellation begins with two representatives, Hedwig and her pain. The symptom chooses to stand behind Hedwig, and when she tries to move away, the representative of her pain follows her. The pain says, "I want to grab you." Hedwig is startled and asks what she has done. When asked whether there is something of note in her background, the client reports that she had an abortion without telling the man involved and that the man had wanted to marry her. I choose a representative for the father of the child and place him next to the symptom. The father of the child is furious and says, "Why did you do that? I loved you so!"

I have Hedwig say to the father of the aborted child, "I am so sorry! I couldn't do anything else." It takes her a while to be able to say this, but the symptom feels superfluous when Hedwig says to him, "I did it. I carry the consequences and I have to pay the full price." The father of the baby draws back sadly.

Immediately following the constellation, Hedwig's pain disappeared and did not reappear during the next two days of the seminar.

The symptoms, here, were an expression of Hedwig's guilt towards the father of the aborted child. She had not told the man of her pregnancy nor of the abortion, which was a betrayal of his fatherhood. The acknowledgement of her "betrayal" balanced the debt and the symptoms were no longer needed.

Symptoms as an Expression of an Interrupted Reaching-Out Movement

Elke, Hay Fever and Her Father

Symptoms: hay fever

Present family: Elke is 56 years old. She is married and has a grown son.

Constellation:

Elke and her hay fever are represented in the constellation. They stand facing one another and it is apparent that there is a deep love between them. When asked, the client reports that she has always had a difficult relationship with her father. I add a representative for her father and place him next to Elke, but at some distance. Elke and her complaint move towards each other and together they turn away from her father. They behave like two lovers.

I ask Elke to stand facing her father and to move slowly towards him. She hesitates and is reluctant to do it. I again encourage her to face him and move towards him. The father's representative also feels uncertain about the movement. After quite a long time, Elke is able to say to her father, "I love you. I long for you." At that point the father also shows some emotion. They embrace and the symptom stands off to one side and feels unnecessary.

The symptom of hay fever was an expression of an interrupted reaching-out movement towards her father. When space was made for the love between Elke and her father, the symptom had no more function in Elke's life.

Heidi, Migraine and Her Mother's Mourning

Symptoms: migraine

Present family: Heidi is 58 years old and married, with four children. She is a psychotherapist.

Family of origin: Heidi's parents are both deceased. When Heidi was seven, her mother was ill with polio but recovered completely. Heidi says she has felt guilty ever since that time.

Symbol: In trance, Heidi sees a skeleton. When she touches the skeleton's hands, its fore arms come alive and she cannot let go of the hands.

First constellation:

Heidi sets up a constellation with representatives for herself and the skeleton. She positions the skeleton behind her representative, who feels a lot of pressure in her head. I move the skeleton to stand facing Heidi. Heidi feels hot, and the skeleton feels rigid. I ask Heidi to bow down to the skeleton. She does so and immediately feels better. Then I have the skeleton bow slightly to Heidi. The representative says, "Now I feel life and happiness." Heidi continues to feel fine.

Process: The next day during the round, Heidi says she is feeling terrible and that she hardly slept during the night. She looks very worn out. I say to her, "Your soul wants to remain true." Heidi nods and says, "My mother always wore black because we were always in mourning for someone." She has no idea, however, why or for whom.

Second constellation:

In this constellation, Heidi, her mother, and the skeleton are represented. The skeleton is looking out from the constellation, and Heidi and her mother stand side by side facing in the opposite direction. I move the skeleton to stand facing the mother. Heidi feels pressure in her head again. Her mother is very uncomfortable and says she feels very angry. The skeleton sways back and forth. I have Heidi and her mother hold hands and bow deeply before the skeleton. The skeleton feels agitated and wants to move away. The representative moves a few steps backwards.

The mother now feels calm. Heidi says, "I feel fine, and I feel close to my mother now." I ask Heidi to look at her mother and say, "It's lovely that you stayed." Heidi and her mother embrace. The symptoms, off to the side, smile benevolently.

My understanding of an interrupted reaching-out movement is that there is a disruption in the nourishing love that usually flows from the mother, father or both towards the child and from the child towards the parents. In this case, the love between the mother and child was interrupted for a period of time because of a potentially fatal disease. That was, at least, how the child interpreted the situation. This led to Heidi's migraines. Why didn't the symptoms disappear when the mother had recovered? There is no scientific explanation, but our experience shows that such childhood traumas often have continuing effects.

The role of the skeleton in the constellation is not quite clear. I would assume that it has to do with something terrible in the mother's family of origin. Heidi's observation that her mother was always in mourning would support this assumption. Both the mother's illness and her difficult fate play important roles here.

There is an additional effect of an interrupted reaching-out movement. When the child's love cannot reach the mother because the mother is entangled in her own system, the soul of the child, out of love for the mother, takes on whatever it is that is binding the mother, or whatever the mother has to carry. This entanglement helps no one, of course, neither mother nor daughter. In Heidi's case it caused an interruption of the love between mother and daughter. This love could only flow again when mother and daughter stood together and bowed before the skeleton, the symbol of Heidi's symptoms, and when Heidi could acknowledge and honour the fact that her mother had actually stayed.

Claudia, Dental Problems and Her Father

Symptoms: caries and recurrent dental problems

Present family: Claudia is 38 years old, single, and has no children. She has never had a significant relationship with a partner.

Family of origin: Her mother lives alone. Her father died when Claudia was twelve. Her mother says that her father was an alcoholic.

Symbol: In trance, Claudia sees a large, white tooth.

Process: In the first round, Claudia says that her issue is to find her right place. I notice that she speaks negatively about her father even though her personal memories of him are positive.

Constellation:

The constellation consists of representatives for Claudia and the tooth symbol. She chooses a man to represent the tooth. The two representatives stand facing each other. Claudia feels her heart pounding and the tooth says, "I would like to be nearer to Claudia." I ask Claudia to move closer to the tooth and to keep looking at him. As she moves nearer, her heart stops racing and she reports a pleasant, warm feeling around her heart. I ask Claudia to bow down before the tooth. As she does so, the tooth lays his hands lovingly on Claudia's head, and she bows more deeply, which both experience as a good movement. The symptom says, "Now I feel fine. I feel my love for Claudia." Claudia straightens up, and she and the symptom embrace. Claudia weeps. In the days that followed, Claudia was calm and relaxed in the group.

In the final round she reports that she now feels she is in her right place, although she hasn't understood a thing and could not explain what happened.

In this constellation there was very little information, and I deliberately stayed with the minimal facts. The work with the symptom had a good effect, and that is what counts. Neither Claudia, nor I, nor the other members of the group were clear about who or what it was that the tooth represented, although I would suspect it was her father. The only person who truly understood, albeit at an unconscious level, was Claudia. It was clear from the effects that her soul understood. The non-intervention of the therapist was especially important in this case.

Isabella, Her Asthma and The Dead

Symptoms: asthma and depression

Present family: Isabella is 78 years old and has been a widow for twenty years. Her husband died in 1981 in a head-on car crash. Of her four children, her only son was killed in 1975 in a diving accident and her three daughters all have families.

In 1998, Isabella was a passenger in a car during a head-on crash. The driver of the car was not injured, but Isabella suffered a broken vertebra in her neck. Ever since that time, she has suffered from asthma. That event also marked the beginning of her depression, which has become worse over time. Isabella came to the constellation group at the suggestion of her eldest daughter.

Constellation:

The constellation consists of two representatives, Isabella and her depression. Isabella's representative spontaneously squats down on the floor, pulls in her head and rolls herself into a ball. She says she feels pushed down into the floor. The representative of her depression bends down to Isabella and pulls her up. As she stands up, she finds it difficult to look at the depression and feels threatened by it. Depression says, "I love you." I ask Isabella to move nearer to depression. They embrace and depression looks very loving. Isabella closes herself off in some way and says, "A part of me is defending itself. I feel a barrier." I ask the client to choose a representative for the barrier. She chooses a man and places him behind her representative. The depression representative and the representative of the barrier both feel uncomfortable.

I move depression and the barrier next to each other, facing Isabella, and all three feel better. I have Isabella bow down to the other two. When she straightens up again, depression says, "Now I would like to pull back," and Isabella says, "I feel drawn to the depression again."

At this point I ask the client about events in her family, and she mentions the death of her son and her husband. I add a representative for death behind depression and the barrier and have Isabella say, "I come willingly to all of you." Depression and the barrier express their discomfort, and both feel cold. They say that they do not want that. When Isabella says, "I will stay for a while and then I will come, too," they both embrace her. Depression stands watching in a friendly manner. The client, Isabella, weeps as she watches from outside the constellation. Her representative releases her embrace and bows. Isabella says, "Now I can breathe freely."

The success of this constellation was amazing. Even after a year, the asthma had not returned, and Isabella was as active as one would expect of a woman her age. She once more took an active interest in her daughters' families as she had done before her accident.

The depression and the barrier, in my opinion, embodied Isabella's deceased son and husband. Which symptom represented which person was secondary and remained unclear. Isabella's car accident was what initiated her symptoms. This event reminded her unconsciously of the sudden deaths of her husband and son, and she had not really completed the process of saying goodbye to them.

Sudden death often leaves too little time for goodbyes. The parting process can be completed only when love can be picked up again at the point where it was interrupted by death.

In Isabella's case it was clear that the bond remained, even when she could say goodbye. When she says, "I will stay a while and then I'll come, too," she can allow herself to feel the pain. It would seem to be a contradiction that letting go is easier when the connection remains. For me, the bond is a sign that everything that was good in the lost relationship can continue to have an effect. This is precisely what makes it easier to let go and what strengthens the desire to live.

Symptoms as a Substitute for Letting Go

Gisela, Stomach-ache and Parting With a Dead Son

Symptoms: chronic stomach pains

Present family: Gisela is 43 years old and married. She has had three children. The middle child was a boy who died at the age of four of a malignant disease. This was ten years ago, and subsequently Gisela has had a lot of psychotherapy. She has decided to do a family constellation because she wants to find more joy with her living children.

Constellation:

The constellation includes Gisela, her symptoms and her deceased son. The symptom representative stands between Gisela and her dead son and says, "I am powerful." I ask Gisela to stand facing her dead son, and I move the symptom off to the side. Gisela tries to express her pain as she looks at her son. "It still hurts so much." Her son looks astounded and replies, "I am doing fine. Leave me in peace." Gisela is able to say to her son, "I let you go." As she says this sentence, the symptom moves away from the two and pulls back.

The chronic stomach pains were an expression of the painful, unresolved bond to her dead son. Gisela recognised that despite her previous psychotherapy, the bond to her dead son was still interfering with her relationships to her living children. Until she did the constellation, she had been unaware of any connection between that and her stomach pains.

The resolution in this form was probably only possible because the loss had occurred ten years earlier, and Gisela had done a lot of grief work in the intervening time. When she experienced her dead son as "doing fine" she was able to let him go. It becomes clear in family constellations that it is the living family members who hang on to the dead, not the other way around. The experience that the dead are "doing fine" often has a freeing effect.

Agnes, Repeated Accidents and Parting with Her Mother

Symptoms: Agnes has suffered for two years from a series of accidents involving a broken arm, a knee injury, and damage to her rib cage.

Present family: Agnes is 65 years old and single, with no children.

Family of origin: Her mother died two years ago. Her father has been dead for twenty years.

Constellation:

The constellation begins with two representatives, one for Agnes and one for her symptoms. The two approach each other lovingly and embrace. Agnes clings to the representative of her symptoms. I choose a representative for her mother and place her next to the symptom. The symptom pushes herself between Agnes and her mother.

I place Agnes facing her mother and she says, "I still could use you here. You were the only one in my life." As she says this, she cries bitterly and her mother embraces her. After a while, I separate the two and ask Agnes to say, "Thank you, it is enough. I let you go." The symptom pulls away.

Two years after the death of her mother, Agnes had still not found the strength to say goodbye to her. The series of accidents, with the accompanying physical pain, was a substitute for the pain of separation from her mother. When Agnes could experience the pain of losing her mother, resolution was possible.

Resolution is always difficult, because it means conclusively relinquishing a certain involvement. In this case, it was Agnes's longing for her mother's love.

Symptoms as Protection from Trauma

Hans, Depression and the Trauma of His Mother's Rape

Symptoms: paralysing depression. The client "plays dead".

Present family: Hans is 59 years old, married, with two grown children. He has come to the group with his wife, who is suffering more from Hans's depression than he is himself. For the sake of his marriage, he has decided to do a constellation.

Family of origin: When Hans was five years old, he had a terrible experience: his mother was raped by Russian soldiers. When one of the soldiers tried to help the woman, his comrades turned on him and killed him. Hans's father died in 1948 while returning from a Russian prisoner of war camp.

Constellation:

A representative for Hans and one for the symptoms are set up in the constellation. The symptoms representative says, "I feel like I'm walking on thin ice. I dare not move." Hans feels terrible. When the symptom comes nearer, Hans feels somewhat better, but is completely unable to move. I add representatives for his mother and his father. The mother is trembling so violently that she can hardly stand. I add a representative for one of the perpetrators and place him facing the mother. He says, "That's the way it is." The mother's trembling lessens a bit. Hans, his mother and the perpetrator lie down next to each other on the floor. The mother begins sobbing.

When asked, the client says that his maternal grandmother committed suicide when his mother was two years old. I put a representative for the grandmother on the floor next to the mother, and the perpetrator alongside her. It is only when I have Hans and his father lie down as well that the mother slowly calms down. I place another representative behind all those lying on the floor to represent the war. The symptoms representative, who has been moving freely about in the meantime, goes to stand opposite the war. Hans lies between his mother and father and remains there until everyone is calm. Then Hans stands up slowly and bows deeply to all the dead: his mother, his grandmother, the perpetrator and his father. When he feels assured that all the dead are "at peace", he turns away. The symptoms prefers to stay near Hans and say, "Now I am a gentle reminder."

At the end of the constellation, I have Hans take the place of his representative, and I also bring Hans's wife into the constellation. I place her facing Hans and ask her to say to him, "I leave your fate with you, with love. I am your wife."

The symptom of "playing dead" protected the client from the trauma from his early childhood that he had not been able to work through. It was too much for the child to live through the horror of his mother being raped and a man being killed in his presence.

In the course of the constellation, Hans experienced the fear of those involved, particularly his mother. The war stood as the origin of all their suffering. Hans was able to watch and feel it all. Bowing down before all the dead and the war made peace possible. The transformation of the symptoms from "playing dead" to "a gentle reminder" allowed resolution in the sense that the past is allowed to exist.

A year later, I met this couple again at a conference. The woman came up to me to tell me happily that her husband had changed considerably. He was smiling as well.

Symptoms as a Substitute for Acknowledging Fate

Johannes, His Knee Pain and His Ill Siblings
Symptoms: recurring pain in his knees

Present family: Johannes is 43 years old and married for the second time. He has two healthy children from his first marriage and no children from the second. The first marriage ended when he left his wife. In addition to the pain in his knees, he is impatient and has a feeling of having to run away.

Family of origin: His father's first wife died, and his father married a second time. He had nine children with his second wife, all of whom except Johannes suffer from polycystic renal disease, a genetic condition.

Constellation:
The constellation includes representatives for all the siblings. I place them in a row according to age. The eldest is to the right. Johannes takes his own place in the constellation rather than using a representative. I ask him to bow deeply before his siblings. Even as he is performing this ritual, he becomes very calm. On the following day, he had no more pains in his knees.

This constellation appears to be very simple. It is, however, extremely difficult to take life's happiness when, as in this case, other members of the family have been so disadvantaged by their fate. In view of the suffering of his siblings, good health brings Johannes a guilty conscience. He acknowledges and honours the fate of his brothers and sisters by bowing deeply to each of them.

Six months later, an acquaintance told me that Johannes was still free of symptoms, so the constellation was a success.

Symptoms as an Expression of Feelings Taken Over from Another

Heinrich, His Depression and His Father's Anger
Symptoms: depression

Present family: Heinrich is 41 years old and married, with a son who is one and a half years old. He has an eleven-year-old daughter from a prior relationship, with whom he has only sporadic contact.

Family of origin: Heinrich's mother had an intimate relationship with her father-in-law, Heinrich's paternal grandfather.

Constellation:
The constellation includes representatives for Heinrich's father, his mother, his paternal grandfather, Heinrich and a representative of the symptoms. Even at the very start of the constellation, there is already evidence of the rage that Heinrich's father feels towards his own father. The symptoms moves to stand next to Heinrich's father and says, "This is my place." As a first step, I place the father opposite the grandfather and ask them both to look each other in the eye. The father's anger slowly subsides. Then I ask Heinrich's father to say to his father: "Thank you for my life. I leave your actions with you." I move the grandfather to an appropriate distance behind his son and position Heinrich facing the two of them. The symptoms continue to stand next to the father.

I give Heinrich a stone and tell him to allow all his anger and depression, everything he has carried for his father, to flow into this stone. When he feels ready, he is to give the stone back to his father.

It takes some minutes while Heinrich concentrates on the stone. He then hands his father the stone without saying anything, but with intense eye contact. The symptoms moves away as they no longer feels needed.

Behind Heinrich's depression lay the repressed rage of his father towards his own father (Heinrich's grandfather), who had had a relationship with his daughter-in-law (Heinrich's mother). Out of love for his father, Heinrich took over his father's depression and the rage behind it. The resolution was completed in two steps. First, the father expressed his justifiable anger to the grandfather and left the responsibility for his actions with him. In the second step, Heinrich expressed his respect for his father and, in the form of a stone, symbolically gave him back the anger and depression that Heinrich had taken over.

A child unconsciously stands by the parent that has suffered some disadvantage, in this case, his father. Heinrich expressed his loyalty by taking over his father's repressed feelings.

Anna, Her Back Pain and Her Aunt and Uncle

Symptoms: back pains that have been resistant to treatment and a death wish

Present family: Anna is 55 years old and married. She had two grown daughters, but the eldest of the two shot herself ten years ago. Anna then attempted suicide twice, and she is now afraid that her second daughter might also kill herself.

Family of origin: Both her parents are dead. Anna's mother was the only surviving child of seven children. Two of the mother's brothers were killed in an accident in their teens, and four children died before they were 10.

Constellation:

A representative for Anna and one for the symptoms begin the constellation. Anna moves slowly towards the symptoms and embraces them with heart wrenching sobs. The symptoms representative returns the embrace and leans against Anna. The next step is to add representatives for the mother, with all her dead siblings around her. I ask the mother to look at each of her brothers and sisters in turn. Deeply moved, she embraces each one of them. Slowly, she becomes calm.

I ask the representatives to open up the circle so that Anna's mother and all her siblings are standing in a row. I put the grandmother behind the row of children and ask Anna's mother to bow to her mother. When she has honoured her in this way, she can lean on her mother and find support there.

Anna's representative stands facing her mother and her mother's siblings. Anna says, "I want to come to you all." I put in a representative for Anna's daughter who killed herself and place her next to her great aunts and uncles. Anna cries and says to her daughter, "I am so sorry," to which her daughter replies, "I did it gladly." I ask the client to take her representative's place in the constellation and to say to her daughter, "I honour your sacrifice." After that, the dead daughter feels well.

At the end of the constellation, Anna bows deeply to all the dead. I bring in representatives for Anna's husband and their second daughter and place them to the left and right of Anna. The three turn around together with the dead standing in a row behind them.

In this case I would like to explain the dynamics of the constellation. On the one hand, Anna's mother took over the grandmother's suffering regarding her six dead children. On the other hand, she was also suffering directly from the death of her brothers and sisters. The result was a great fear of life, connected with a longing for death. This is a phenomenon that is often seen when someone is a lone survivor. As a result, Anna took over the suffering and the death wish of her mother. In the case of her daughter's suicide, my interpretation would be that Anna's daughter was taking Anna's place in death.

The resolution here was completed in steps. Anna's mother first acknowledged the suffering of her mother, Anna's grandmother. Then, Anna honoured her daughter's suicide. Finally, she acknowledged the fate of all the dead by bowing down to them. After that, she could turn to her present, her husband and her living daughter.

Andrea, Her Asthma and the Women in Her Family

Symptoms: bronchial asthma

Present family: Andrea is 45 years old and has two daughters, aged twelve and fourteen. She was divorced when her daughters were three and five. She started suffering from asthma for the first time after her divorce. She then lived with a man who died of a heart attack a year ago at the age of 49.

Family of origin: Her great-grandmother was a single mother with two children, who immigrated to the United States. No one knows what she did there, but after many years, she came back with a lot of money, bought a house and lived unmarried until her death.

Andrea's grandmother was divorced when Andrea's mother was ten years old. Andrea's mother was divorced after 25 years of marriage. Andrea was divorced after seven years of marriage.

Symbol: In a symptom trance, Andrea sees clouds gathering as before a thunderstorm. When Andrea bows before the clouds, everything dissolves and she has an asthma attack.

Process: In the first round, Andrea says that her issue is to look at why the generations of women in her family always separate from their men. I ask her why she left her own husband, and I notice her deep disrespect for her husband. I ask, "Who started this contempt of men?" Andrea does not answer. I suggest that she set up representatives for her husband and her father, next to each other. Behind her husband, she is to put representatives of his father and grandfather, and behind her father, representatives of his father and grandfather. Then I ask her to bow down to all the men. Andrea is very reluctant to do this. I ask what is fighting against it and she answers, "Everything!" My response is, "Then, it will continue in the same way."

First constellation:
This constellation includes Andrea, her ex-husband, the two daughters and her symptoms (asthma). Both of the daughters are standing with their backs to Andrea, looking the same direction. The ex-husband is somewhat off to the side, where he feels uncomfortable. The symptoms are standing behind Andrea and feel powerful. When I ask Andrea to turn to her ex-husband, the symptoms feel relieved. I leave the constellation at that point for the time being.

I give Andrea an exercise, which is to look at every man she sees on the street and to say to herself, "Men are good." In addition I ask her to complete a written assignment: "What do I value in my husband, and what do I value in my father?" Since this contempt for men has been around for many generations, I give her this assignment in order to open up other, new perspectives. At the same time, she can have the experience of looking at men from a different point of view.

Such interventions can make a person aware of entanglements. In this case, the entanglement involves taking over contemptuous feelings from the women in the family, and the exercise allows her to create her own view of men.

Process: The next day during the round, Andrea reports that when she did the assignment, her asthma got worse. Besides that, she had rung up her father to tell him that she would like to make peace with him. He was very happy but afterwards she felt like a traitor.

I ask Andrea to imagine her father and mother standing next to each other and to say to both of them, "Thank you; because of your love I am alive." When I ask how it is to say that, Andrea reports feeling nothing. I ask her which of her parents would feels happier to hear this thank you and she replies, tearfully, "My father." I have her imagine only her mother and say to her, "You loved him. I love him, too." In her imagination, Andrea repeats this sentence but feels her mother's rejection very clearly. I leave it there and tell Andrea that it will take some time.

Andrea is true to her mother, grandmother and great-grandmother in her contempt of men. Her asthma began when she divorced her husband. In the constellation, the symptoms feel relief when Andrea turns to her ex-husband, which means that the symptoms are an expression of the interrupted reaching-out movement to her husband. The symptoms are the price she is paying for remaining true to the women on her maternal side.

The resolution would be for Andrea to give up her loyalty to this image of men held by her mother, grandmother and great-grandmother and to turn towards her ex-husband. This would certainly be possible only if she is first able to let in her love for her father. She can only allow this love if her mother agrees. When she had a friendly phone conversation with her father, she felt guilty. In order to let in the love for her father, she has to overcome her guilty conscience towards her mother. Andrea found that her mother could not agree to this love, because she, in turn, was loyal to her own mother. For this reason, resolution is not yet possible. In this case it would probably be necessary to uncover the great-grandmother's secret, since both Andrea's mother and grandmother have remained loyal to this woman.

The story of this client is an illustration of the way an illness (in this case, asthma) may pay the price for loyalty to the original family system. Seen from the viewpoint of the client's soul, the formulation might be, "I would rather have asthma than give up my loyalty to the women in my family and to their view of men."

Symptoms in Abstract Constellations

Elisabeth, Her Panic and Compulsive Behaviour and Her Mother
Symptoms: panic attacks and compulsive behaviour

Present family: Elisabeth is 35 years old, and single, with no children.

Family of origin: Her mother is 66 years old and healthy. Her father died of a heart attack two years ago at the age of 66.

Process: Elisabeth has been in individual therapy for four years. During this time she has done three family constellations in which it was always clear that something terrible must have happened in her mother's family system. When Elisabeth looked into it, she found that her maternal grandfather had run a chemical factory during the Second

World War. Despite great effort, the client was unable to learn any details about her mother's family. In the course of her therapy, Elisabeth became more and more certain that she has taken over something from her mother's family system. There has been no resolution, and her incapacitating symptoms have improved only mildly. I suggest trying another family constellation.

Constellation:

Two representatives are included in the constellation, Elisabeth and her symptoms. The client chooses a woman to represent her symptoms. She places the two representatives facing each other at a distance of about two meters. During the entire constellation, the symptoms representative looks at Elisabeth in a very friendly manner, holding her hands out invitingly. Elisabeth's representative's whole body is trembling, and when she tries to take hold of the symptoms' outstretched hands, she keeps jerking back in panic.

It takes about fifteen minutes, without a word being spoken, before Elisabeth can calmly take hold of the symptoms' hands and return the friendly gaze. When Elisabeth and her symptoms have looked lovingly at each other for a few minutes as they hold hands, I end the constellation. Since that time, Elisabeth has had no further symptoms.

I very consciously chose not to do yet another constellation of the family of origin. I proceeded on the assumption that the panic represents a guilt taken over from the family system of her mother. This has hindered the flow of love towards her mother.

The resolution lay in allowing love to flow between Elisabeth and her symptoms. It is not clear who or what the symptoms stand for, nor is it necessary to interpret it in any way. I expressly forbid the group members to speak about it, even amongst themselves. In order for the effects of the process to go on having an impact, it is essential not to dissipate what has happened by talking about it.

Josef, Back Pain and The Mirror

Symptoms: lower back pain

Present family: Josef is 42 years old and single, with no children. When he was 28, his best friend committed suicide, and since that time Josef has suffered from lower back pain.

Trance: In symptom trance, Josef sees a mirror as a symbol of his back pain.

Constellation:

There are two representatives, one for Josef and one for the mirror. Josef places his representative and that of the mirror facing each other. Both feel terrible. I ask Josef to bow down to the mirror, but it is difficult for him. The longer Josef remains bowed down, the better the mirror feels, and it slowly draws back. Now, Josef feels like something is missing, but he doesn't know what it is. When I ask the client, there seems to be no relevant information apart from what is in the constellation. I add a representative for fate behind the mirror. Josef declares that he wants to go and join fate. Fate embraces Josef for a long time, and Josef feels safe and secure in this embrace. The mirror pulls further away. I end the constellation at this point.

Because of Josef's medical history, I came to the conclusion that his friend's suicide must have had some meaning in Josef's life besides grief at his death. His back pain started at the time of this suicide.

I followed my intuition in setting up a representative for fate although I couldn't explain exactly why. Josef felt love towards fate behind the mirror (the symbol of his pain). Who or what that fate was embodying is unclear. In this case, an explanation is not important because of the effects. Following the constellation, the client was free of back pain.

Hilde, Nausea and Her Parents' Fate

Symptoms: continuous nausea

Present family: Hilde is 45 years old, married and has had four children. Her first child died two months after birth.

Family of origin: Hilde's grandmother was Jewish and was hidden during the war by her daughter, the client's mother. Her father was a perpetrator in the war. The details of his deeds are not available. Her parents married after the war, in about 1950.

Process: The client has already had a lot of psychotherapy, and her life has improved a lot as a consequence. Her bouts of nausea, however, have continued and are so incapacitating that she has decided to do another constellation.

Constellation:

The constellation includes representatives for Hilde and for her symptoms. The symptoms' representative states that something is missing. I choose an additional representative for fate and add this person to the constellation. The symptoms and fate stand facing each other. Hilde stands off to the side and does not feel much of anything. I ask the symptoms to bow down to fate, but that proves impossible. Then I bring in a representative for Hilde's mother and father. I place fate and symptoms next to each other facing the mother and father. I ask the parents to bow to fate and the symptoms. The symptoms representative feels superfluous and pulls away. Fate becomes very calm. The father says that he has the feeling he would have to bow down for "an eternity". Both parents kneel down before fate. Hilde is standing off to the side crying in relief. This image allows her to leave her parents' fate with them.

Her nausea went away only slowly, and it took about a year before she was completely free of symptoms. During this time, she kept the image in her mind of her parents bowing down to fate. Hilde's nausea could be interpreted as a sign of her interfering in the fate of her parents. The constellation made clear that the parents humbly agreed to their own fate, and this image had a healing effect.

I would describe Hilde as a child of reconciliation. The marriage of her Jewish mother to her father, who was probably a perpetrator, was an act of reconciliation.

In many constellations it is clear that reconciliation and peace between victims and perpetrators is only possible when they have found their way to each other. This is particularly clear in working with the dead. In Hilde's case, the reconciliation occurred between living people, her parents. When she was able to see and experience that in the constellation, she could thankfully take her life, anchored in this reconciliation.

Sabine, Her Depression and the Prisoners

Symptoms: depression that is experienced as crippling

PresentFamily: Sabine is 43 years old and single, no children.

Symbol: In symptom trance two knights in armour appear, holding an imprisoned woman between them.

Constellation:

The constellation consists of representatives for the client, the two knights and their prisoner. Sabine places the woman between the two knights and her representative opposite them. The knights feel terrible, and the prisoner wants to pull Sabine over to her. Sabine's representative pulls back from this. Even when I ask Sabine to slowly approach the prisoner and look at her, there seems to be no relationship between them.

I give the client a stone and tell her to let all the incapacitating effects flow into the stone in whatever way she feels them. When she is ready, she is to give the prisoner the stone and say, "I leave this with you." As Sabine hands the stone to the prisoner, everyone feels a sense of relief. I turn Sabine around so she is standing with her back to the others. She still feels pressure on her back and, therefore, is unable to move away. She is not yet free to live her own life.

Since the pressure is a sign of something unresolved, I turn Sabine around to face the other three again. She feels grief and says that she feels small and wants to cuddle up to the prisoner. I have her say to the imprisoned woman, "Out of love for you, I remain small and weak and I will continue to carry it with you." At this point I end the constellation.

The resolution of returning the stone that I tried at the beginning of the constellation was premature. Sabine's soul was not yet ready for that resolution, and the client could not separate from the prisoner. She was still waiting for something from her, because a love remained interrupted.

Constellations with symptoms and symbols of symptoms have the advantage that the intimate sphere of the client, the client's system, and fate are protected by the abstract nature of the work. I find working with symbols especially helpful because these symbols appear in trance, directly from the unconscious, similar to the way dreams operate. The therapist should be very cautious in interpreting symbols or their connection to family members. Rational explanations are usually meaningless to the client, but the soul understands what it is all about. The effects are visible, as was true in example of Josef's experience with back pains and the mirror.

Symptoms as a Substitute for a Parent's Previous Partner

Peter, His Binge Eating and His Mother's First Love

Symptoms: binge eating

Present family: Peter is 35 years old, single and has no children. He has been in a long-term relationship for the past ten years.

Family of origin: Peter's parents have been married for 40 years. His mother had a significant love relationship before this marriage, but could not marry that man for religious reasons. His mother is a Mennonite, and her boyfriend was Catholic. She married Peter's father one year after her separation from the other man.

Symbol: In symptom trance the client sees a dancing bear, and he wants nothing to do with it.

Constellation:

The constellation includes representatives of Peter, the bear, his father and his mother. The client places the bear near his representative and they both look at his mother. The mother and father are standing facing one another, and neither looks at Peter or the bear. The representative of the bear is furious and says that he wants the mother to look at him. I put the bear to the right of the mother and Peter's father on her left side. All three now look at Peter. The mother does not feel at all well standing next to the bear and wants her son. I have Peter tell his mother, "I am happy to replace your lover. You are my one and only." The representatives of Peter and his mother agree and say that it feels good like that. I leave it like this. This statement of bonding marks the high point of the energy because it is an expression of love.

The constellation makes clear that Peter is a substitute for his mother's first, great love. The resolution, which was not yet possible in this case, would be for his mother to acknowledge her first love. In addition, Peter would have to say to his mother, "I am only your son." This case illustrates a child representing a parent's previous, unacknowledged partner. This is an expression of the child's love for the parent who had to give up a previous relationship, regardless of the reasons for it.

Gerhard, His Neurodermatitis and His Mother's First Husband

Symptoms: neurodermatitis and feelings of shame related to the disease

Present family: Gerhard is 41 years old. At one time he had planned to become a priest, but shortly before his ordination he was dismissed. He was married once, but the marriage only lasted for six months.

Family of origin: Gerhard's parents are both still alive. His mother is Hungarian and was married to someone else in Hungary before her marriage to Gerhard's father. She fled Hungary in 1956. Gerhard does not know what happened to his mother's first husband.

Process: During the trance session at the beginning of the group, I notice that Gerhard is having difficulty inhaling. I suggest that he close his eyes, consciously breathe in deeply, and say quietly, "I am alive!" In doing this exercise, Gerhard sees himself climbing a mountain and breathing deeply. This feels very good to him.

In the next round, Gerhard mentions that he always feels a sense of shame because of his neurodermatitis. I ask him who is more ashamed, his father or his mother? He spontaneously answers, "My mother!"

Constellation:

The constellation includes representatives for Gerhard, his father, and his mother. When he has set up the three representatives, he chooses another representative for his mother's first husband. Gerhard and his mother stand facing each other, his father is somewhat off to the side and his mother's first husband is between Gerhard and his mother. His mother and her first husband embrace spontaneously. Gerhard looks away and says to his mother, "I don't want you to embrace your first husband." I choose a representative for neurodermatitis and put this representative behind Gerhard's mother. She says, "This symptom feels very familiar to me." When she looks at her second husband and her son, she feels ashamed. I move the mother's first husband next to her, on her right and Gerhard's father on her left at some distance. Gerhard faces them. I ask the first husband to say to the mother, "We belong together." The mother says, "I feel guilty," and the father says, "I feel small." Gerhard says, "I feel empty." I move the mother nearer to father so that her first husband is further off to the side. The first husband begins to tremble violently. The mother says to Gerhard, "Only the first one is important to me. I am sorry." Gerhard and his mother embrace.

Gerhard feels a pain in his chest and tells his mother, "You have used me." She answers, "That's true, but now I'm sorry." I suggest that Gerhard tell her, "I give you thanks for my life and I honour your love for your first husband." His mother is crying as she says, "It still hurts so." I have Gerhard say, "Now I leave you with your great love and go to my father." The symptoms representative, who has been standing behind the mother the whole time, now pulls back.

Gerhard stands by his father but does not feel a sense of closeness. I notice in this that something essential to the resolution is missing. The mother's first husband is still standing alone, trembling. I ask Gerhard's father to bow to his wife's first husband and say to him, "You were the first, and I am only the second." The father feels relieved, but the first husband continues to tremble violently. Neither the love of the mother nor the respect of the father brings this man relief. Therefore, there must have been something terrible in his history. I add a representative for death and place him behind the first husband, who immediately feels calm.

I ask the mother to take her son by the hand and stand in front of her first husband. She says to her son, "This is my first husband. He had to die. His death has nothing to do with you." Then I bring Gerhard's father to join them. Gerhard, his father, and his mother all bow deeply before the first husband and death. The first husband then draws back with death. Gerhard leans back on his parents and breathes deeply and calmly.

In this constellation it was very clear that the son was representing a parent's previous partner. The symptoms of neurodermatitis became superfluous when Gerhard acknowledged his mother's first husband and honoured her love for that man. From the first husband's reactions, even after being recognised and honoured and Gerhard's lack of closeness with his father, it was clear that this resolution was not enough.

As Bert Hellinger has said, "To become a man, a man has to move out of his mother's sphere of influence and into his father's."

As long as his mother's first husband was doing poorly, Gerhard could not move into his father's sphere of influence. His life up to this point had been lived accordingly. He had not been able to form a satisfying, long-term relationship, and he had severe physical limitations, including neurodermatitis and breathing difficulties, that seemed to have no organic basis. It was only possible for him to take his life fully when he, his father and his mother all paid their respect to his mother's first husband.

Gerhard's case illustrates the process of a constellation and its changing dynamics. On the basis of the information that his mother had been previously married, it was easy to suspect that Gerhard was representing her first husband. The reactions of the representatives led us much further.

Symptoms in Couples' Relationships

Rainer, His Rage and Nina with Her Melancholic Depression and Neck Pains

Symptoms: Nina: melancholic depression and neck pains. Rainer: outbursts of temper.

Present family: Nina is 35 and Rainer is 37, and they have three children together. They would like to finally get married, but it just doesn't happen. They don't know any reason for this, or the reason remains unconscious. This issue brings them to do a family constellation.

Families of origin: Nina's parents are Austrian citizens. Her maternal grandfather died at a very early age. Her maternal grandmother almost bled to death during the birth of Nina's mother. Nina's maternal great-grandmother, (this grandmother's mother) died in childbirth.

Rainer's paternal grandparents fled from Palestine to Austria with their son, Rainer's father. Rainer's father married in Austria. Although Rainer was born in Austria, he feels like a Palestinian.

Constellation with Nina:

The constellation includes Nina, her mother and her grandmother, who lost her husband at a young age. It is clear that Nina feels drawn to her grandmother. Her mother shows no feelings. When the client, Nina, is asked, she says that her grandmother almost bled to death during the birth of Nina's mother, and her great-grandmother died in childbirth. I choose a representative for the great-grandmother and place the four women one behind another. Nina stands in front, then her mother, then her grandmother and then her great-grandmother.

I ask Nina's representative to describe her feelings. She says that she feels no connection to the women behind her.

I move Nina to face the other three women. The mother starts crying. I move her next to Nina. Nina says that she feels drawn to the great-grandmother. I move the grandmother next to the mother so that the three generations of women are facing Nina's great-grandmother. I ask them to bow down before the great-grandmother. Afterwards, they all feel comfortable.

I repeat the earlier positioning, so that Nina is standing at the front of the line of females in the previous generations. She leans back against her mother and says: "Now I can feel my strength and, most importantly, the strength of my mother." Following this, I have Nina take her representative's place in the constellation. She looks radiant.

Process: The following day, Rainer talks about his inexplicable outbursts of rage. As he tells the story of his father and grandparents having to flee from Palestine, Nina begins to cry with heart-rending sobs. I ask Rainer if he knows whom Nina is crying for. He looks very surprised and answers, "She is crying for me and my father."

Constellation with Rainer and Nina:
I place the two clients, Rainer and Nina, facing one another. I have Nina say to Rainer, "I am crying your tears." Rainer shows no reaction. I choose a man to represent Palestine and place him behind Rainer. Rainer says, "Now I feel heavy and sad." Nina feels much better. I turn Rainer to face the representative of Palestine. Rainer begins to cry, and the two spontaneously embrace. Rainer bows down to Palestine, and Palestine gives him his blessing. I ask Rainer to turn around again. He looks at Nina, with Palestine behind him. The couple beam at one another. Nina says spontaneously, "I like seeing you like this." I ask her to tell Rainer: "I honour your homeland, and I leave your grief with you."

I add a woman to represent Austria and place her behind Nina. I have Rainer say, "Thank you. It is good to be with you."

The organiser of this seminar told me that the couple married two months later.

I will begin with an interpretation of Nina in this constellation. She was able to feel the strength of the feminine from her ancestors when the women had all honoured the death of the great-grandmother in childbirth. Nina had been carrying her mother and grandmother's pain from the death of the great-grandmother. She was also helping Rainer to carry his pain over the loss of his homeland. Unconsciously, Nina felt the pain behind his rage. Unlike Rainer, who could not express his pain, Nina broke into tears as he told his story.

I had the clients experience the second constellation directly, without the use of representatives. It was only when he was confronted with his homeland, Palestine, that Rainer could allow his pain to surface. I chose a male representative for Palestine, because I suspected that Rainer was carrying his father's pain at the loss of his homeland. I interpreted his rage as a substitute for feelings of pain. In psychological terminology, the anger was a secondary feeling, and the pain was a primary feeling. When space was made for Rainer's pain and that of Palestine (his father), Rainer could look at his wife with his homeland at his back. Nina's country, Austria, stood behind her. At this point, Rainer could take Nina as his wife and could respect Austria as his new home and not just a country of asylum.

Rosa, Her Intestinal Cancer and Richard's Depression

Symptoms: Rosa: metastasised intestinal cancer. Richard: crippling depression.

Present family: Rosa and Richard have been married for 40 years. It is the only marriage or important relationship for both of them. They have two daughters. The elder daughter died of breast cancer six months before the seminar. Two months after her death, the younger sister was in a serious car accident and was slowly recovering from her injuries at the time of the seminar. A year and a half after her daughter got cancer, Rosa developed cancer as well. Robert said that he had come to the seminar because of his love for his wife.

Rosa's family of origin: Rosa's mother had been in a convent for six months before she got married because she was not allowed to marry her first great love. When Rosa was thirteen, her father died of a heart attack. She had a younger brother who died at birth.

Richard's family of origin: Richard's mother separated from his father when Richard was ten. Richard didn't see his father again until ten years later and said that he felt disgusted by his father. In the meantime, his father has died. Further information about Richard's original family system has emerged only slowly in the course of various constellations and in response to intensive, repeated questions. His maternal grandmother died when Richard's mother was sixteen. His mother's brother was accidentally shot and killed while hunting when he was a teenager. His mother's sister died young and was said to have had an illegitimate child that she gave away.

Process: In the first round Richard is the first to speak. He finds it difficult to speak and is fighting back tears. "We have had to endure a lot during the last year. Rosa has had three operations, our daughter died and our other daughter was in an accident ... it was just too much." Richard weeps. Next to him, Rosa sits calmly and quietly. When it is her turn, she says very calmly, "I have cancer that has metastasised and I am in great pain."

First constellation with Rosa:

Representatives are set up for Rosa and her dead daughter. They stand next to each other, looking in the same direction. I choose a woman to represent cancer and place her opposite the two women so that they are looking directly at cancer. Both experience this as a relief. The representative of cancer feels pressure in her head. As the first step, I place a representative for Rosa's dead brother next to her. Rosa and her brother feel fine with this, but nothing changes for the cancer representative. Then I choose a representative for the first great love of Rosa's mother. This produces no change for Rosa, her daughter or cancer. I remove this man from the constellation.

As a second step, I move Rosa to face her dead daughter, with cancer standing next to her daughter. I ask Rosa to say to her daughter, "I am coming." The daughter spontaneously replies, "I don't want that." I ask Rosa to say, "Thank you for your sacrifice." The daughter answers, spontaneously, "I did it gladly." Rosa and her daughter embrace and they both feel very good. Nothing has changed for the representative of cancer, and she still has an uncomfortable pressure in her head.

Process: The second day, Rosa says during the round that her pain has increased massively and she feels extremely ill.

Second constellation with Rosa:

This constellation begins with representatives for Rosa and her pain. Rosa places the pain behind her own representative. I ask the representatives to move in any way that feels right to them, and Rosa steps behind the pain and lays her head on the representative's neck. I choose a representative for death and place him opposite the other two. Rosa immediately feels better. She pushes the representative of pain off to the right and looks directly at death. Death says, spontaneously, "I have warm feelings and I have lots of time." Rosa approaches death, looking at him as she moves. As she does that, the representative of pain feels superfluous and pulls back. Rosa bows deeply before death and puts both arms around him. She says, "That feels so good. I feel unbelievably strong." I stop the constellation there. I then read Bert Hellinger's story:

The Guest

Where the Wild West once was, a man with a backpack was wandering through the lonely land. He had walked for hours, the sun was high in the sky, and his thirst was growing. He saw a farmhouse on the horizon and thought, "Thank God, at last another human being in all this loneliness! I'll stop there and ask for a drink, and perhaps we'll sit on the porch and talk a while before I set off again." He imagined how nice that would be.

But as he drew nearer the house, he saw the farmer working in the garden and he began to have second thoughts. "He's probably very busy and doesn't have time. If I bother him, he'll feel annoyed and think I'm rude." When at last he reached the garden gate, he just waved to the farmer and walked on.

The farmer had seen him in the distance and felt pleased. "Thank God," he had thought, "at last another human being in all this loneliness! I hope he comes here. We could drink something together, and perhaps sit on the porch and talk a while before he goes on his way." The farmer went into the house and prepared something cool to drink.

But, as the walker came closer, the farmer began to think, "He's most certainly in a hurry. If I speak to him, I'll put him in an awkward situation. He may feel that I'm pushing myself on him. But, perhaps he's thirsty and will come over on his own. The best thing would be for me to go into the garden and act busy. Surely he'll see me and if he wants anything, he'll ask me." When the walker only waved in passing, the farmer thought, "What a pity!"

The walker walked on and on. The sun was hot and his thirst was growing. It was hours before he saw another house on the horizon. He thought to himself, "This time I will approach the farmer, even if I'm a nuisance to him. I am so thirsty that I simply must have something to drink."

As the farmer saw the walker in the distance, he thought to himself, "Oh God, just what I don't need right now when I have so much to do! I don't have time to take care of anyone right now." He continued to work without looking up.

The walker watched the farmer go out into the field and he followed him and said, "I am very thirsty. Could you please give me something to drink?" The farmer thought, "I can't send him away; it wouldn't be right." So he took the stranger into the house and gave him something to drink.

The stranger said, "I saw your garden. It's clear that someone has worked here who truly understands gardening and loves plants." The farmer replied, "So you like gardening?" They sat down on the porch and talked for a long time. Finally, the stranger said, "I must be on my way now." The farmer protested, "But the sun is getting low. Stay the night here with me. We'll breakfast early in the morning and you can be off then." The stranger agreed.

As evening came, they sat on the porch and watched the vastness of the western sky transfigured in the evening light. In the darkness, the stranger talked about how his world had changed once he had begun to be aware of someone accompanying him step by step. He said that at first he couldn't believe that the other was always there, and when he stopped, the other stopped and when he went on, the other went on as well. It had taken a while before he understood who his companion was. "My constant companion is my death," he said. "I have grown so accustomed to his presence that I would miss him now if he weren't there. He is my truest and best friend. When I don't know what's right or what to do, I stop a while and wait for his answer. I have surrendered myself to him, and I know he's there and I am here. Without clinging to my own desires, I wait for his message to come to me. When I am centred and have courage, a word comes from him to me like a lightning flash illuminating the dark, and I become clear."

The farmer found this talk strange, and he gazed silently into the night. After a long time, he saw his own death, his own companion. He bowed his head to him. As he paid his respects to his own death, it was as if the rest of his life were changed. It became as precious as the love that anticipates a parting, and like such love, it was filled to overflowing.

In the morning, they broke their fast together, and the farmer said, "Even though you are leaving, my friend remains." They went outside, shook hands, and said goodbye. The stranger went on his way and the farmer returned to his field.

Process: On the third day, Richard is very upset during the round and wants to set up a constellation of his present family system.

First constellation with Richard:
The constellation includes representatives for Richard, Rosa and their two daughters. The representatives initially stand in a zigzag row, all facing the same direction. When I ask the client, Richard, if there has been any unusual fate in his family, there is no information. I choose a representative for a secret and place this representative facing the others. Richard does not want to look at the secret and tells it to "get out." The secret feels threatened and moves back. I turn the secret around so that he is looking outwards, and I move the dead daughter and Rosa to stand in a line behind him. The secret spontaneously says, "This is good. We can go like this." Richard is standing somewhat off to the side. He says that he feels quite alone, but fine. I leave the constellation at this point. Rosa, who is sitting in the group outside the constellation, is furious.

Process: On the fourth day, Rosa looks completely transformed. She says in the round that she feels strong and is experiencing no pain. Richard offers new information that he has received from his aunt, his mother's sister.

Second constellation with Richard: He sets up the entire family on his mother's side with the uncle who died, the aunt who died and the child that was given away. I add a representative for the secret. I try one combination after another in turn but no one seems to have any relationship with the secret, or vise versa. This constellation has no results.

Process: In a later round, Richard says that he now knows that he has a big problem with this secret. I ask him what else has happened in the family. He says that his mother left his father when Richard was ten, and his mother had always talked badly about his father. He had seen his father only three times before his father died, and the sight of him made him feel sick.

Third constellation with Richard:
The constellation begins with representatives for Richard and his father. Richard places his father looking outwards and his own representative looking in the opposite direction. I move Richard to stand facing his father and wait. I ask both to look each other in the eye. Then I ask Richard to say to his father, "I have found you." It takes a long time before he is able to say this. Richard weeps and the two

embrace for a long time. I add a representative for Richard's mother. She spontaneously says, "That's a weight off my chest."

Process: Following this constellation, Rosa asks if it is possible that she has been carrying Richard's pain regarding his father. I tell her, "Yes, that is possible. That is why it is important for you to leave his pain with him. Additionally, it is probable that you are suffering for someone in your family." Rosa very quickly says, "Yes, for my father. He was given away by his parents and died of a heart attack at the age of 49."

Third constellation with Rosa:
The constellation consists of representatives for Rosa and her father. She places them facing each other. Rosa says, "I don't want to look." She moves one step back and says again, "I don't want to see your suffering. I would rather carry it for you." The father feels touched. The client, Rosa, who is outside the constellation, nods vehemently. I ask the father to say to his daughter, "You are my lovely Rose." They embrace. I have Rosa take her representative's place in the constellation. She weeps profusely in her father's arms and then slowly becomes calm.

I give Rosa a stone and tell her to let everything she has carried in her love for her father flow into this stone and then to hand it to him when her soul is ready. She adds, "I leave your suffering with you." Afterwards, I ask her to say to her father, "Thank you for my life. Please give me your blessing if I stay." Her father gives her his blessing, and I end the constellation.

Three moths after the seminar, I got a letter from Richard telling me of his wife's death. She had died peacefully, and he was coping with it better than he had expected to. He thanked me for my work with them.

What I found particularly touching during this four-day seminar was the great love that was palpable between this man and wife. One thing that stood out in their relationship was that both Rosa and Richard had lost their fathers at an early age. Perhaps this fact had made it easier for them to understand one another. Because of the complexity of both family systems and the large number of people who had died young, a different approach to the constellation might have been considered. It looked as though the death of their daughter had something to do with the secret in the father's family system, and Rosa had followed along in that. Although Rosa's positive reaction to death made it clear to me that she wanted to die, I looked further for another solution. It was difficult for me to take in this image, but Rosa had a different experience. She felt much more comfortable with death after the constellation, and the most important effect was that she could die without pain.

Mathilde, Her Chronic Bladder Infections and Matthias and His "Blackouts"

Symptoms: Mathilde: chronic bladder infections

Matthias: "Blackouts" following alcohol consumption

Present family: Mathilde is 52, and Matthias is 56. They have been married for 28 years and have two grown children. After the death of her father, who had lived with them for 15 years, Mathilde left her husband and went to live in the south of France.

Families of origin: Mathilde's mother died fifteen years ago and her father came to live with her and Matthias. Her father died two years ago, at the age of 98. Her father's first wife, who was his great love, died in 1945.

Matthias's mother died of cancer when Matthias was 23. His father died ten years later. Matthias is the youngest of six brothers.

Process: Matthias began individual therapy because of his blackouts following alcohol consumption. In this state, he showed signs of self-destructiveness that were almost suicidal, but afterwards, he would not be able to remember anything. His wife repeatedly threatened to leave him. When she finally left him, I was able to convince Matthias to do a family constellation. In the constellation of the present family system, it was clear that there was no hope for their relationship. Mathilde was bound in some entanglement in her family system. When Matthias wrote to Mathilde about what had happened in the constellation, her interest in their relationship was re-awakened.

Four weeks later, we set up a constellation of the original family system. Matthias said that his mother's sister had been taken to Russia after the war. She did not return until 1950 and was very disturbed. She lived with the family until she died at a young age. In the constellation, Matthias expressed his respect for the fate of his aunt.

Following the constellation, Matthias felt completely free. He began to enjoy his life once again, and he had no more blackouts when he drank alcohol. He trusted himself again to have a glass of wine. He had a brief relationship with another woman. Mathilde was so shaken up by this new side of her husband that began to emerge that she also decided to do a family constellation.

It was quickly clear in the constellation of Mathilde's family of origin, that she had replaced her father's first wife. When she recognised the connection, she felt free. She decided to return to her husband and has had no further bladder infections.

I got a letter a half a year later telling me that both of them were happier together than they had ever been before in their lives. The most positive result was that they were now able to enjoy their sex life. Since bladder infections usually have something to do with female sexuality, it is understandable that their sex life could be experienced freely only when the identification with her father's first wife had been resolved.

The case of Mathilde and Matthias is an example of how entanglements in the original family system can burden the relationship with a current partner and how a resolution can release happiness in the relationship.

Closing Comments

The Courage to Look

I often hear people say that they have wanted to do a family constellation for a long time, but did not feel confident enough. It is easy to see this reluctance as a fear of losing one's place of belonging in the family system. Many clients feel cautious, particularly in a group situation, and they usually express this uneasiness at the beginning of a seminar.

When I begin a seminar, I have people go into trance and give their fears some space. In their imagination, in trance, clients can ask their families for permission to do a family constellation. In this way, their reluctance is taken seriously and we give their fears a place. Still, everyone has to develop a certain amount of courage to take part in a constellation. People have to get past their fears of uncovering family secrets that may have been taboo up to this point. Looking at the entanglements in one's own family is often uncomfortable and sometimes painful and shocking as well.

In many cases, what prompts people to do a family constellation is the pressure of their own, personal pain. I often wonder if it is really necessary for the pressure of the pain to first get so unbearable, because it means that clients often wait a very long time before they are led to do a constellation.

Although many of these cases appear very dramatic, it is certainly not a requirement that one has some terrible fate in the family history in order for there to be a resolution in a constellation. It is much more common that so-called normal problems and everyday crises point to unresolved issues in the family. Here too, we run up against barriers that are constructed because of loyalties that protect one's belonging to a family.

There are conspicuously more women than men who come to do family constellations. This imbalance corresponds to the situation in other approaches to psychotherapy. There are many factors that contribute to this phenomenon. For one, it is more acceptable for women to admit that they are suffering than it is for men. For another, women are more likely than men to feel responsible for relationships running smoothly. They tend to "manage" the psychological health in relationships and in the family. The third reason may lie in the structure of our society, which can still be described as male-dominated. Men often have more avenues open to them for compensating their problems. Conflicts are often not brought out in the family, but rather pushed into some other area such as sports or the work world.

I have observed these dynamics repeatedly, and my therapeutic goal is to make it possible for men as well as women to increase their responsibility and awareness in family relationships.

Courage in Holistic Psychosomatics

Courage is required of the doctors and therapists as well: the courage to depart from the mainstream and take up new approaches to treatment. On the one hand, psychosomatics is increasingly accepted among my colleagues. On the other hand, this acceptance is usually limited to complaints and symptoms with no discernible organic cause—the so-called "functional" disturbances. It is only when all of the tests and treatment methods of traditional medicine have failed that psycho-therapy is recommended. It is only at this point that patients come to do a family constellation.

To change this habitual practice of trying psychotherapy only when all else fails requires changing the attitude of patients and physicians. For the patients, a diagnosis of an organic disease is often a relief. In line with the "orders of love" they remain true to their family system and consciously hand over the responsibility for their health to doc-tors.

From what I have observed, entanglements are often deeper and more serious in cases of organically diagnosed illnesses and therefore more urgently in need of treatment. Because I know and value the achievements of traditional medicine, the work with family constella-tions is a wonderful complement for me. In this context, I would like to repeat, "Body and mind are the same." One of the reasons I have written this book is the hope that this approach will spread and find more acceptance in the field of traditional medicine.

Courage to Love

Life arises through love. Love is what drives our longings and hopes and therefore, the foundation of all entanglements. This has slowly become clear to me during my 16 years of working with family constellations as taught by Bert Hellinger.

I would go so far as to view symptoms and disease as expressions of our bonds of love, the love for all the members of our "clan". The bonds of love strive to balance any terrible fate. The bonds of love function on the basis of bonds order and balance. When the balance is also seen as recompense in the system, then illness and symptoms are paths towards reconciliation. Many family constellations illustrate these dynamics. They are always unconscious and can be described as a process:

Through the family constellation, the first step is to bring into consciousness that which is unconscious.

The second step is to confront what becomes visible and to acknowledge that the symptoms or illness are an expression of the bonds of love.

The third step makes this recognition experiential. It has to be acknowledged that terrible and sad things are also a result of love in family systems. Making space for the feelings that are connected to this recognition can lead to reconciliation with all the burdens the client has suffered from, including symptoms and illness. The family constellation serves to prepare the path. When that succeeds, you can thankfully take what you have received, agree to your fate, and live a fulfilled life. When you are open to this form of love, you set a process in motion that will accompany you for the rest of your life.

References

Bauriedl, T. (1997): Wege aus der Gewalt. Analyse von Beziehungen. Freiburg (Herder).

Bökmann, M. (1999): Mit den Augen eines Tigers. Heidelberg (Carl-Auer).

David-Néel, A. (1998): Die geheimen Lehren des tibetischen Buddhismus. Satteldorf (Adyar).

Dilts, R. B., S. Smith, T. Hallbom (1990): Beliefs – pathways to health and well being. Portland, OR (Metamorphous Press).

Erickson, M. H., E. L. Rossi, S. L. Rossi (1976): Hypnotic realities. The induction of clinical hypnosis and forms of indirect suggestion. New York (Irvington).

Hellinger, B., G. ten Hövel (1999): Acknowledging What Is. Conversations with Bert Hellinger. Phoenix (Zeig, Tucker & Co.).

Hellinger, B. (2001): Die größere Kraft. Bewegungen der Seele bei Krebs. Heidelberg (Carl-Auer).

Hellinger, B. (1996): Die Mitte fühlt sich leicht an. Vorträge und Geschichten. Munich (Kösel).

Hellinger, B. (2006): No waves without the ocean. Experiences and thoughts. Heidelberg (Carl-Auer).

Hellinger, B. (2001): Entlassen werden wir vollendet. Munich (Kösel).

Hellinger, B. (2000): Religion, Psychotherapie, Seelsorge. Gesammelte Texte. Munich (Kösel).

Hellinger, B. (1997): Schicksalsbindungen bei Krebs. Ein Buch für Betroffene. Heidelberg (Carl-Auer), 4th ed. 2004.

Hellinger, B. (2002): On life and other paradoxes. Aphorisms and little stories. Phoenix (Zeig, Tucker & Theisen).

Hellinger, B., G. Weber, H. Beaumont (1998): Love's hidden symmetry. What makes love work in relationships. Phoenix (Zeig, Tucker & Co.).

Imber-Black, E. (1998): The secret life of families. How secrets shape relationships – when and what to tell. London (Thorsons).

Imber-Black, E. (ed.) (1993): Secrets in families and family therapy. New York/London (Norton).

Imber-Black, E., J. Roberts, R. A. Whiting (eds.) (1988): Rituals in families and family therapy. New York/London (Norton).

Kast, V. (1982): Wege aus Angst und Symbiose. Märchen psychologisch gedeutet. Freiburg i. Br. (Walter).

Madelung, E. (1998): Trotz und Treue. Zweierlei Wirklichkeit in Familien. Heidelberg (Carl-Auer), 2nd ed. 2003.

Neuhauser, J. (ed.) (2001): Supporting love. How love works in couple relationships. Bert Hellinger's work with couples. Phoenix (Zeig, Tucker & Theisen).

O'Conner, J., J. Seymour (1990): Introducing neuro-linguistic programming. The new psychology of personal excellence. Wellingborough (Crucible).

Satir, V. (1988): The new peoplemaking. Mountain View, CA (Science and Behavior Books).

Schlippe, A. von, J. Schweitzer (1996): Lehrbuch der systemischen Therapie und Beratung. Göttingen (Vandenhoeck & Ruprecht).

Selvini, M. (1992): Mara Selvinis Revolutionen. Die Entstehung des Mailänder Modells. Heidelberg (Carl-Auer).

About the Authors

Ilse Kutschera, M. D., was born in Vienna, Austria in 1936. As a young woman in war-scarred Europe, she was strongly encouraged to find a practical profession in which she could support herself quickly. As a result, she became a medical technician and subsequently spent two years in the United States in this capacity. She then followed her heart's desire and went back to university in Graz to study medicine. She worked as a physician until 1998, when she retired from her position as head of a rehabilitation clinic to devote her time solely to her private psychotherapy practice. During her career, she had developed a keen interest in psychotherapy and trained in various approaches including primal therapy, transactional analysis, gestalt therapy, NLP and Bert Hellinger's constellation work. This book is an expression of her passionate interest in integrating the work of psychotherapy and classical medicine.

Christine Brugger, was born in Germany in 1962. She completed a degree in landscape engineering to embark on a zigzag career that led through complementary health fields, public relations and advertising to her present position as the head of a radio station in the East Tyrol in Austria. She lives with her husband, two children and dog. Through her contact and friendship with Dr. Ilse Kutschera, she became interested in the project of writing about the constellation work in the medical field. The book is the result of many interviews, discussions and recorded case histories.

Bert Hellinger

No Waves Without the Ocean

Experiences and Thougths

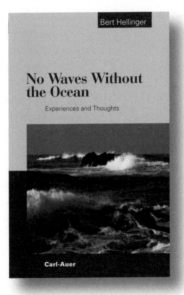

311 Seiten, Pb, 2006
ISBN 10: 3-89670-548-2
ISBN 13: 978-3-89670-

This volume represents the core of Bert Hellinger's thinking and insights based on his experience with family constellations work. Set out as a reference book, it gathers together, for the first time, previously unpublished material, introductions and summaries, illustrative comments and answers to questions gathered from his many seminars and workshops, as well as several interviews and one complete lecture.

The organisation of chapters according to topic allows for easy access, and many, for example, "Family Constellations and Movements of the Soul", represent the most comprehensive handling of the subject to date.

Whether this book is read cover-to-cover or used as a reference book on specific topics, the authority and eloquence of Bert Hellinger's formulations and his range of experience offer rich rewards for the reader.

www.carl-auer.com